Workout

Mathematics

Grade 6

Triumph Learning®

A Haights Cross Communications ®®® Company

Workout, Mathematics, Grade 6
241NA
ISBN-10: 1-59823-953-8
ISBN-13: 978-1-59823-953-9

Cover Image: © Purestock/Punchstock

Triumph Learning® 136 Madison Avenue, 7th Floor, New York, NY 10016
A Haights Cross Communications, Inc. company

Printed in the United States of America.

10 9 8 7 6 5 4 3 2 1

Dear Student,

Are you a math champion?

You will be when you use

Workout!

Getting in shape is easy. Just complete the lessons inside.

So, on your mark, get set –

Work OUT!

Table of Contents

Algebraic Concepts

Data Analysis and Probability

Math Words

LESSON 1 Greatest Common Factor and Least Common Multiple

When you find greatest common factors and least common multiples, remember these words:

factor number that divides evenly into another number

greatest common factor (GCF) the greatest number that divides evenly into two or more numbers

multiple the product of a number and a counting number

least common multiple (LCM) the least number that is a multiple of two numbers

Example 1 Find the GCF of 8 and 12.

Step 1 List factors.

8: 1, **2**, **4**, 8

12: 1, **2**, 3, **4**, 6, 12

> **THINK** Common factors of 8 and 12 are in bold.

Step 2 Find the GCF.

2 and 4 are common factors.

So, the GCF of 8 and 12 is _____.

Example 2 Find the LCM of 8 and 12.

Step 1 List multiples.

8: 8, 16, **24**, 32, 40, **48**, . . .

12: 12, **24**, 36, **48**, 60, . . .

> **THINK** Common multiples of 8 and 12 are in bold.

Step 2 Find the LCM.

24 and 48 are common multiples.

So, the LCM of 8 and 12 is _____.

 **List the factors of each number.**

1. 16 _____ **2.** 20 _____ **3.** 28 _____

Find the GCF.

4. 8 and 10 _____ **5.** 9 and 11 _____

6. 30 and 35 _____ **7.** 16 and 24 _____

8. 10 and 20 _____ **9.** 21 and 27 _____

Find the LCM.

10. 6 and 15 _____ **11.** 3 and 12 _____

12. 5 and 7 _____ **13.** 9 and 15 _____

14. 4 and 6 _____ **15.** 12 and 20 _____

Solve.

16. Hot dogs are sold in packages of 10 and hot dog buns are sold in packages of 8. Vincent bought the same number of hot dogs and buns. What is the smallest number of hot dogs Vincent could have bought?

_____

17. To simplify the fraction $\frac{16}{36}$, Jasmine divided numerator and denominator by their GCF. What did Jasmine divide by?

_____

Ask Yourself

1.
Which is a factor of 16?
6, 8, or 32

4.
What number divides both?
2, 3, or 4

10.
Which is a multiple of 6?
2, 3, or 12

16.
Which do you use? GCF or LCM

On Your Own!

Circle the answer for each question.

1. What is the GCF of 20 and 25?

   A. 1

   B. 3

   C. 4

   D. 5

2. What is the LCM of 8 and 9?

   A. 1

   B. 36

   C. 48

   D. 72

3. What is the GCF of 16 and 24?

   A. 16

   B. 8

   C. 4

   D. 2

4. What is the LCM of 5 and 9?

   A. 45

   B. 15

   C. 14

   D. 1

5. The greatest common factor of Ferdy's age and Vyada's age is 6. What could their ages be?

   A. 24 and 32

   B. 12 and 18

   C. 6 and 20

   D. 2 and 3

6. Ceil is thinking of two numbers. Their least common multiple is 60. What could the numbers be?

   A. 6 and 10

   B. 8 and 10

   C. 10 and 12

   D. 20 and 40

7.   The numbers 73 and 127 are both prime numbers.

   Part A   Find the GCF of 73 and 127.

   _____

   Part B   Explain how you found the GCF of 73 and 127.

   _____

   _____

   _____

 Fill in the blanks.

8.   1, 2, 3, 4, 6 and 12 are the _____ of 12.

9.   7, 14, 21, 28, and 35 are _____ of 7.

10.   3 is the _____ _____ _____ of 6 and 9.

11.   18 is the _____ _____ _____ of 6 and 9.

LESSON 2 ▶ Divisibility Rules

 **Review It!**

When you work with divisibility rules, remember this word:

divisible a number is divisible by a second number if the second number divides evenly into the first number

20 is divisible by 5 because 20 ÷ 5 = 4.
20 is not divisible by 7 because 20 ÷ 7 = 2 R6.

Check whether 750 is divisible by 2, 3, 5, 9, or 10.

Step 1　Check the divisor 2.

750 is an even number. Every even number is divisible by 2.

Step 2　Check the divisor 3.

To check 3 use this method: Add the digits in 750: $7 + 5 + 0 = 12$

Since 12 is divisible by 3, so is 750. ◀ · ▸ **THINK** This is the divisibility rule for 3.

Step 3　Check the divisor 5.

If the ones digit is 0 or 5, it is divisible by 5.

Step 4　Check the divisor 9.

To check 9 use this method: Add the digits in 750: $7 + 5 + 0 = 12$ ◀ · · · ·

Since 12 is not divisible by 9, 750 is not divisible by 9.

REMEMBER If the sum of the digits is divisible by 9, then the number is divisible by 9.

Step 5　Check the divisor 10.

If the ones digit is 0, it is divisible by 10.

So, 750 is divisible by _____, _____, _____, and _____.

Check whether each number is divisible by 2, 3, or 5.

1. 21 _____   **2.** 12 _____   **3.** 19 _____

4. 510 _____   **5.** 123_____   **6.** 1,000 _____

7. 675 _____   **8.** 809 _____   **9.** 935 _____

Check whether each number is divisible by 9 or 10.

10. 738 _____   **11.** 927 _____   **12.** 5,230 _____

13. 60 _____   **14.** 743_____   **15.** 85 _____

16. 315 _____   **17.** 3,450 _____   **18.** 621 _____

Solve.

19. The digits in a three-digit number are 9, 5, and 4. Use these digits to make a three-digit number that is divisible by 5 and by 9.

_____

20. The smallest three-digit number is 100. What is the smallest three-digit number that is divisible by 3 and 10?

_____

1.
What type of number is 21?
even or odd

10.
What is the sum of the digits?
17, 18, 19

19.
What must the ones digit be?
4, 5, 9

On Your Own!

Circle the answer for each question.

1. Which number is divisible by 3?

   A. 111

   B. 121

   C. 131

   D. 133

2. Which number is **not** divisible by 5?

   A. 95

   B. 500

   C. 505

   D. 551

3. By which number is 7,132 divisible?

   A. 2

   B. 3

   C. 5

   D. 9

4. Which number is **not** divisible by 9?

   A. 909

   B. 1,234

   C. 3,456

   D. 9,009

5. By which numbers is 762 divisible?

   A. 2, but not 3

   B. 3, but not 2

   C. both 2 and 3

   D. neither 2 nor 3

6. Mel's address on Oak Street is divisible by 3 and 5, but not by 9 or 10. Which of these could be Mel's address?

   A. 35 Oak Street

   B. 135 Oak Street

   C. 435 Oak Street

   D. 750 Oak Street

7. The largest three-digit number is 999. What is the largest three-digit number that is divisible by both 5 and 9?

   A. 995

   B. 990

   C. 985

   D. 980

8.   **Part A** Explain how you check to see if a number is divisible by 9.

_____

_____

_____

      Part B Use your method from Part A to test whether 58,734 is divisible by 9.

_____

_____

_____

Math Words   **Fill in the blanks.**

9.   To use the _____ _____ for 5, look at the last digit of a number.

10.   Since there is no remainder when you divide 48 by 3, 48 is _____ by 3.

11.   Every _____ number is divisible by 2.

12.   A number is divisible by 10 if its _____ _____ is 0.

13.   A number is divisible by 3 if the _____ of its digits is divisible by 3.

LESSON 3 — Exponents

Review It! When you use exponents, remember this word:

exponent a number that tells the number of equal factors

exponent
$5^3 = 5 \times 5 \times 5$ (5 is used as a factor 3 times).

Example 1 **Write the following using an exponent: $8 \times 8 \times 8 \times 8$**

Step 1 Write the number that is being multiplied by itself. _____

Step 2 Count the number of equal factors.
Write that number as an exponent after the repeated number.

8 ———

> **REMEMBER** Count how many times 8 is a factor.

So, $8 \times 8 \times 8 \times 8 =$ _____.

Example 2 **Find the value of $10 - (n^2 - 2 \times n + 1)$ if $n = 3$.**

Step 1 Rewrite the expression with 3 in place of n.

$10 - (n^2 - 2 \times n + 1) = 10 - (3^2 - 2 \times 3 + 1)$

Step 2 Follow the order of operations inside the parentheses.

> **REMEMBER** The Order of Operations: (1) Parentheses, (2) Exponents, (3) Multiply and divide from left to right, (4) Add and subtract from left to right.

$= 10 - (9 - 2 \times 3 + 1)$ Write the exponents as multiplication.

$= 10 - (9 - 6 + 1)$ Multiply from left to right.

$= 10 - (4)$ Add and subtract from left to right.

$=$ _____

So, if $n = 3$, $10 - (n^2 - 2 \times n + 1) =$ _____.

 **Try It!** Use exponents to write an equivalent expression.

1. 7×7

2. $2 \times 2 \times 2 \times 2 \times 2 \times 2$

_____

_____

3. $10 \times 10 \times 10 \times 10$

4. $9 \times 9 \times 9 \times 9 \times 9$

_____

_____

1.

Which number will be the raised exponent?

2 or 7

Find the value of each.

5. 3^4

6. 11^3

7. 7^3

_____

_____

_____

8. 5^4

9. 4^2

10. 10^3

_____

_____

_____

5.

Which should you find?

$3 \times 3 \times 3 \times 3$

$4 \times 4 \times 4$

Find each value if $x = 2$ and $y = 3$.

11. x^3

12. y^2

_____

_____

13. $20 - x^2$

14. $5 \times y^2$

_____

_____

15. $y^3 - 21$

16. $(5 \times x - 2 \times y)^2$

_____

_____

11.

Which is the correct substitution?

3^2 or 2^2

On Your Own!

Circle the answer for each question.

1. What is another way to write
   5 × 5 × 5?

   A. 3^5

   B. 5^2

   C. 5^3

   D. 5^5

2. What is another way to write 3 × 3 × 3 × 4 × 4 using exponents?

   A. $3^3 \times 4^2$

   B. $3^3 \times 2^4$

   C. $(3 \times 4)^2$

   D. $(3 \times 4)^5$

3. Which of the following shows exponential notation correctly?

   A. $2 \times 2 \times 2 \times 2 \times 2 = 5^2$

   B. $8 \times 8 \times 5 = 8^5$

   C. $9 \times 9 \times 9 \times 9 = 9^2$

   D. $3 \times 3 \times 3 \times 3 = 3^4$

4. The formula for the area of a square is area(A) = side × side. What is the correct way to write the formula using exponents if each side equals 7?

   A. $A = 2^7$

   B. $A = 2^2$

   C. $A = 7^2$

   D. $A = 7^7$

5. Find the value of $a^2 - 6$ if $a = 5$.

   A. 1

   B. 4

   C. 16

   D. 19

6. Find the value of $2x^3 - 4x$ if $x = 3$.

   A. 6

   B. 42

   C. 69

   D. 152

7. Find the value of $4(2x - 7)^2$ if $x = 5$.

   A. 24

   B. 36

   C. 144

   D. 152

8. Find the value of $x^3 + 3x - 4$ if $x = 10$.

   A. 56

   B. 326

   C. 1,026

   D. 1,996

9. Using a factor tree, Lil found the prime factorization of 360 to be
2 × 2 × 3 × 5 × 2 × 3.

Part A How can she write the product using exponential notation?

_____

Part B Use what you know about exponents to explain how you know your
answer in Part A is correct.

_____

_____

_____

_____

 Draw a line to match each expression to its equivalent
expression using different notation.

10. 3×3 $\qquad$ 2×3

11. $2 \times 2 \times 2$ $\qquad$ 3^2

12. $3 + 3$ $\qquad$ 2^3

LESSON 4 — Properties of Numbers

Review It!

When you identify which property to use, remember these words:

Commutative Property if two numbers are added or multiplied, the result is the same if their positions are switched

Associative Property if three numbers are added or if three numbers are multiplied, the result is the same if the grouping of numbers is changed

Identity Property a number remains unchanged if 0 is added to it. A number remains unchanged if it is multiplied by 1.

Which property does this example show?

$$8 \times 9.1 = 9.1 \times 8$$

Step 1 Compare the left side of the equation to the right side.

Is the order of the numbers switched? _____

Step 2 What operation does the problem use? _____

Step 3 Use your answers to Steps 1 and 2 to choose the property:

Commutative Property of Multiplication

Associative Property of Multiplication ◀·············· **THINK** The positions of the factors are switched.

Identity Property of Multiplication

So, $8 \times 9.1 = 9.1 \times 8$ is an example of the _____ Property of _____.

 Write the property shown for each.

1. $1.8 \times 7.4 = 7.4 \times 1.8$ **2.** $29 + 0 = 29$

_____   _____

3. $56 + 0.2 = 0.2 + 56$ **4.** $0.35 \times 1 = 0.35$

_____   _____

5. $(4 + 10) + 6 = 4 + (10 + 6)$ _____

6. $9 \times (7 \times 22) = (9 \times 7) \times 22$ _____

Use the named property to complete the number sentence.

7. Identity Property of Multiplication, $17 \times \underline{} = 17$

8. Associative Property of Addition,

$38 + (12 + 9) = (\underline{} + 12) + \underline{}$

9. Commutative Property of Multiplication, $\frac{1}{2} \times 14 = \underline{}$

10. Identity Property of Addition, $\frac{5}{8} + \underline{} = \frac{5}{8}$

11. Commutative Property of Addition, $3.6 + 7.4 = 7.4 + \underline{}$

12. Associative Property of Multiplication,

$(12 \times 0.4) \times 5 = \underline{} \times (0.4 \times \underline{})$

Ask Yourself

1. Which type of property is represented? Associative Commutative Identity

7. What is the identity number for multiplication? 0 or 1

On Your Own!

Circle the answer for each question.

1. Which shows the Identity Property of Addition?

   A. $20 \times 1 = 20$

   B. $\frac{3}{4} \times 0 = 0$

   C. $4.8 + 0 = 4.8$

   D. $16 - 16 = 0$

2. Which shows an example of the Commutative Property of Multiplication?

   A. $12 \times \left(\frac{5}{6} + \frac{4}{5}\right) = \left(12 + \frac{5}{6}\right) \times \frac{4}{5}$

   B. $12 \times \left(\frac{5}{6} \times \frac{4}{5}\right) = \left(12 \times \frac{5}{6}\right) \times \frac{4}{5}$

   C. $12 \times \frac{5}{6} = \frac{5}{6} + 12$

   D. $12 \times \frac{5}{6} = \frac{5}{6} \times 12$

3. Which property does this example show?

   $$9 + (10.4 + 10) = (9 + 10.4) + 10$$

   A. Associative Property of Addition

   B. Associative Property of Multiplication

   C. Commutative Property of Addition

   D. Identity Property of Addition

4. Which one of these is **not** true?

   A. $0 + 0 = 0$

   B. $(8 \times 7) \times 1 = 8 \times 7$

   C. $1 + 0 = 1$

   D. $1 \times 0 = 1$

5. Which one of these is the same as $8 + (4 + 10)$?

   A. $8 \times (4 + 10)$

   B. $8 + (10 + 4)$

   C. $(8 + 4) + (8 + 10)$

   D. $8 + (4 \times 10)$

6. Which one of these is the same as $7 \times 1 \times 9$?

   A. 7×9

   B. $7 + 1 + 9$

   C. $7 \times 0 \times 9$

   D. $7 \times 1 + 7 \times 9$

7. **Part A** Meryl said that $(78 - 18) + 2 = 78 - (18 + 2)$. Is she correct?

_____

Part B Use what you know about properties to explain why Meryl is correct or incorrect.

_____

_____

_____

 Draw a line to match each property to its example.

8. Associative Property of Multiplication $\qquad$ $230 + 110 = 110 + 230$

9. Identity Property of Multiplication $\qquad$ $7.25 \times 1 = 7.25$

10. Commutative Property of Addition $\qquad$ $0 + 58 = 58$

11. Identity Property of Addition $\qquad$ $(2.4 \times 1.5) \times 4 = 2.4 \times (1.5 \times 4)$

LESSON 5 — Mixed Numbers and Improper Fractions

Review It! When you work with mixed numbers and improper fractions, remember these words:

mixed number a number with a whole number part and a fraction part

$$6\frac{3}{4}$$

fraction a number that compares a part to a whole or a part to a part

$$\frac{5}{8}$$

improper fraction a fraction with a value greater than or equal to 1

$$\frac{6}{5}, \frac{9}{4}, \frac{10}{5}$$

What improper fraction do the shaded figures stand for?

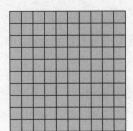 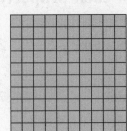 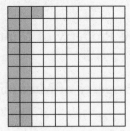

Step 1 Write the mixed number.

2 whole squares are shaded.

$\frac{21}{100}$ of the third square is shaded.

So, the mixed number is $2\frac{21}{100}$.

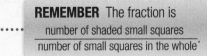

REMEMBER The fraction is

$$\frac{\text{number of shaded small squares}}{\text{number of small squares in the whole}}.$$

Step 2 Write the mixed number as an improper fraction.

Find how many small squares are in 2 whole squares. $2 \times 100 = 200$

Add that to the number of small squares in the fraction. $\frac{200}{100} + \frac{11}{100} = $ _____

So, the shaded figures stand for the improper fraction _____.

Write each mixed number as an improper fraction.

1. $1\frac{5}{8}$

2. $2\frac{1}{5}$

3. $5\frac{1}{2}$

_____

1.

How many parts are in a whole?

5 or 8

4. $3\frac{1}{4}$

5. $4\frac{2}{3}$

6. $6\frac{3}{8}$

_____

7. $5\frac{3}{4}$

8. $7\frac{3}{8}$

9. $3\frac{5}{6}$

_____

7.

After dividing, the remainder is the numerator. Which number is the denominator?

3 or 5

Write each improper fraction as a mixed number.

10. $\frac{5}{3}$

11. $\frac{9}{2}$

12. $\frac{10}{7}$

_____

10.

How many 3s go into 5?

1, 2, or 3

13. $\frac{11}{3}$

14. $\frac{28}{5}$

15. $\frac{37}{9}$

_____

On Your Own!

Circle the answer for each question.

Use the figures for Questions 1 and 2.

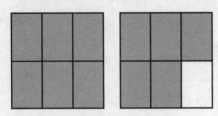

1. What mixed number is shown in the figure?

A. $\frac{5}{6}$ C. $1\frac{5}{6}$

B. $1\frac{1}{2}$ D. $2\frac{5}{6}$

2. What improper fraction does the figure stand for?

A. $\frac{1}{11}$ C. $\frac{11}{12}$

B. $\frac{6}{11}$ D. $\frac{11}{6}$

3. Which improper fraction is equal to $7\frac{2}{9}$?

A. $\frac{72}{9}$ C. $\frac{27}{9}$

B. $\frac{65}{9}$ D. $\frac{79}{2}$

4. Which improper fraction is equal to $5\frac{3}{7}$?

A. $\frac{38}{7}$ C. $\frac{53}{7}$

B. $\frac{57}{3}$ D. $\frac{36}{7}$

5. Which improper fraction is equal to $3\frac{5}{6}$?

A. $\frac{18}{6}$ C. $\frac{35}{6}$

B. $\frac{23}{6}$ D. $\frac{18}{5}$

6. Which is equal to $1\frac{1}{5}$?

A. $\frac{11}{5}$ C. $\frac{6}{5}$

B. $\frac{5}{11}$ D. $\frac{5}{6}$

7. Which improper fraction is equivalent to $10\frac{3}{4}$?

A. $\frac{103}{4}$

B. $\frac{43}{4}$

C. $\frac{34}{4}$

D. $\frac{17}{4}$

8. Which improper fraction is equivalent to $8\frac{2}{3}$?

A. $\frac{82}{3}$

B. $\frac{26}{3}$

C. $\frac{25}{3}$

D. $\frac{13}{3}$

9. Lance baked brownies for a school bake sale. The shaded figures stand for the brownies sold.

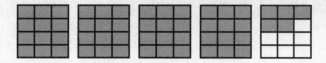

Part A   What mixed number do the shaded portions stand for? Use what you know about mixed numbers to explain why your answer is correct.

_____

_____

_____

Part B   Write your mixed number in Part A as an improper fraction.

_____

 Draw a line to match each word to its meaning.

10. whole number   a number with a whole number part and a fraction part

11. fraction   a counting number, including 0

12. mixed number   a fraction with a value greater than or equal to 1

13. improper fraction   a number that compares a part to a whole

LESSON 6 Fraction-Decimal Equivalences

Review It! When you convert between fractions and decimals, remember these words:

decimal a number with a decimal point

equivalent numbers in different forms that have the same value

numerator the top part of a fraction

denominator the bottom part of a fraction

repeating decimal numbers to the right of a decimal point that repeat continuously in a pattern

---

Example 1 Write $\frac{7}{20}$ as a decimal.

Step 1 Divide the numerator by the denominator. ◄......... **THINK** Add 0s to the right of the decimal point in 7.

$$
\begin{array}{r}
0.3\,5 \\
20\overline{)7.0\,0} \\
\underline{6\,0} \\
1\,0\,0 \\
\underline{1\,0\,0} \\
0
\end{array}
$$

So, $\frac{7}{20} =$ _____.

Example 2 Write 0.16 as a fraction.

Step 1 Use place value to write a decimal as a fraction. ◄.......... **REMEMBER** Use the LAST place value to read a decimal number.

$0.16 = \frac{16}{100}$

Step 2 Write the fraction in simplest form.

$\frac{16}{100} = \frac{16 \div 4}{100 \div 4} = \dfrac{\square}{\square}$ ◄......... **REMEMBER** Divide by the greatest common factor of 16 and 100.

So, $0.16 =$ _____.

Write the fraction as a decimal.

1. $\frac{9}{10}$ _____
2. $\frac{13}{25}$ _____
3. $\frac{7}{8}$ _____

4. $\frac{5}{16}$ _____
5. $\frac{29}{40}$ _____
6. $\frac{4}{5}$ _____

7. $\frac{1}{25}$ _____
8. $\frac{9}{20}$ _____
9. $\frac{33}{80}$ _____

Write the decimal as a fraction in lowest terms.

10. 0.44 _____
11. 0.2 _____
12. 0.125 _____

13. 0.63 _____
14. 0.625 _____
15. 0.02 _____

16. 0.004 _____
17. 0.029 _____
18. 0.75 _____

Solve.

19. A medicine has 0.375 milligrams of its active ingredient. Write this amount as a fraction in simplest form.

_____

20. A recipe uses $\frac{1}{4}$ teaspoon of pepper. Write this amount as a decimal.

_____

Ask Yourself

1. Which operation can you use? — or ÷

10. How do you read 0.44? tenths or hundredths

19. What is a factor of both 375 and 1,000? 2, 3, or 5

On Your Own!

Circle the answer for each question.

1. How is $\frac{17}{100}$ written as a decimal?

   A.   17,100

   B.   1.7

   C.   0.17

   D.   0.017

2. How is $\frac{9}{16}$ written as a decimal?

   A.   0.5625

   B.   0.565

   C.   0.916

   D.   1.778

3. How is 0.55 written as a fraction?

   A. $\frac{55}{1}$

   B. $\frac{55}{10}$

   C. $\frac{11}{25}$

   D. $\frac{11}{20}$

4. How is 0.024 written as a fraction?

   A. $\frac{1}{24}$

   B. $\frac{1}{41}$

   C. $\frac{1}{42}$

   D. $\frac{3}{125}$

5. A house for sale is on "a quarter of an acre" of land. How is this amount written as a decimal?

   A.   0.025 acre

   B.   0.25 acre

   C.   2.5 acres

   D.   25 acres

6. A piece of fabric is 0.875 yard long. How is this length written as a fraction?

   A. $\frac{7}{8}$ yard

   B. $\frac{5}{6}$ yard

   C. $\frac{4}{5}$ yard

   D. $\frac{3}{4}$ yard

7. Pilar is using directions to find her friend's house. The directions say, "After you make the right turn, drive $\frac{3}{4}$ of a mile."

Part A Write this distance as a decimal.

_____

Part B Write $\frac{3}{4}$ as a decimal to the nearest tenth.

_____

Use the fraction-decimal equivalence shown below to answer Questions 8–12.

$$\frac{17}{20} = 0.85$$

8. The digit 5 is in the _____ place.

9. The number 17 is in the _____ of the fraction.

10. The digit 8 is in the _____ place.

11. The number 20 is in the _____ of the fraction.

12. The period between 0 and 8 is called the _____ _____.

LESSON 7 > Percents

Review It! When you work with percent, remember this word:

percent a ratio of a number to 100

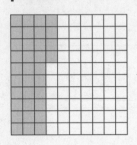

Since 34 of 100 squares are shaded, 34% is shaded.

Write 28% as a fraction in simplest form and as a decimal.

Step 1 Write the percent in the numerator and 100 in the denominator.

$$28\% = \frac{28}{100}$$

> **THINK** Percent means *per hundred*.

Step 2 Write the fraction in simplest form.

$$\frac{28}{100} = \frac{28 \div 4}{100 \div 4} = \frac{\boxed{}}{\boxed{}}$$

> **REMEMBER** Divide by the greatest common factor of 28 and 100.

Step 3 Rewrite the fraction as a decimal.

$\frac{28}{100}$ is read as *28 hundredths*.

That means that $\frac{28}{100} = 0.$ _____.

So, 28% written as a fraction in simplest form is _____ and written as a decimal is _____.

Write the percent as a decimal.

1. 13% ____   **2.** 77% ____   **3.** 4% ____

Write the percent as a fraction in lowest terms.

4. 9% ____   **5.** 84% ____   **6.** 50% ____

Write the decimal as a percent.

7. 0.43 ____   **8.** 0.05 ____   **9.** 0.6 ____

Write the fraction as a percent.

10. $\frac{39}{100}$ ____   **11.** $\frac{91}{100}$ ____   **12.** $\frac{1}{100}$ ____

Solve.

13. A real estate agent gets a 3% bonus when he sells a house. Write this percent as a decimal and as a fraction in simplest form.

_____

14. DVDs are on sale for 25% off this week. Write this percent as a decimal and as a fraction in simplest form?

_____

 Ask Yourself

1. What goes in the denominator? 1, 10, or 100

4. Do 9 and 100 have any of the same factors? yes or no

7. In which place is the 3? tenths or hundredths

10. Percent is a ratio of a number to ____? 1, 10, or 100

13. What will the denominator be? 3, 10, or 100

On Your Own!

Circle the answer for each question.

1. How is 45% written as a decimal?

   A. 0.045

   B. 0.45

   C. 45.0

   D. 4,5000

2. How is 20% written as a fraction?

   A. $\frac{20}{1}$

   B. $\frac{2}{1}$

   C. $\frac{1}{50}$

   D. $\frac{1}{5}$

3. How is $\frac{11}{100}$ written as a percent?

   A. 1,100%

   B. 11%

   C. 1.1%

   D. 0.11%

4. How is 0.9 written as a percent?

   A. 0.9%

   B. 9%

   C. 90%

   D. 900%

5. In a group of 100 students, 40 ride to school in a car. What percent of the students in this group ride to school in a car?

   A. 2.5%

   B. 4%

   C. 25%

   D. 40%

6. An agent charges a rate of 0.06 to her clients. How is this rate written as a percent?

   A. 0.06%

   B. 0.6%

   C. 6%

   D. 60%

7. Paul needs to write the fraction $\frac{3}{4}$ as a percent, but $\frac{3}{4}$ does not have 100 as its denominator.

Part A Show the steps you use to change $\frac{3}{4}$ to a fraction with a denominator of 100.

_____

_____

_____

Part B Use your work from Part A to write $\frac{3}{4}$ as a percent.

_____

Fill in the blanks.

8. A percent is a ratio of a number to _____.

9. If you write 34% as a decimal, 3 is in the _____ place and 4 is in the _____ place.

10. _____ means *per hundred*.

11. If you write 7% as a fraction, the numerator is 7 and the _____ is 100.

LESSON 8

Ordering Whole Numbers, Fractions, and Decimals

Review It! To order fractions and decimals, you first need to write them in the same form so you can compare them.

Order these numbers from least to greatest.

$$3 \qquad 3\frac{5}{8} \qquad 3\frac{2}{3} \qquad 2\frac{7}{8}$$

Step 1 Compare the whole number parts.

$2 < 3$, so, the least number is _____.

Also, 3 has no fractional part, so $3 < 3\frac{5}{8}$ and $3 < 3\frac{2}{3}$.

The first two numbers are _____ and _____, in that order.

Step 2 Next, compare the fraction parts of $3\frac{5}{8}$ and $3\frac{2}{3}$.

The least common denominator of $\frac{5}{8}$ and $\frac{2}{3}$ is 24.

$$\frac{5}{8} = \frac{5 \times 3}{8 \times 3} = \frac{15}{24}$$

$$\frac{2}{3} = \frac{2 \times 8}{3 \times 8} = \frac{16}{24}$$

Since $\frac{15}{24} < \frac{16}{24}$, $3\frac{5}{8} \bigcirc 3\frac{2}{3}$. ◄⋯⋯⋯⋯⋯⋯⋯⋯⋯⋯⋯⋯⋯⋯⋯⋯

> **THINK** When the denominators are alike, compare numerators.

So, the order from least to greatest is _____ , _____ , _____ , _____ .

Try It! Compare. Write <, >, or =.

Ask Yourself

1. $\frac{3}{4}$ ◯ $\frac{2}{3}$

2. $\frac{7}{8}$ ◯ $\frac{9}{10}$

1. Which is the least common denominator? 7 or 12

3. $\frac{4}{5}$ ◯ $\frac{5}{8}$

4. $2\frac{3}{10}$ ◯ $5\frac{1}{2}$

5. $7\frac{2}{3}$ ◯ $7\frac{5}{8}$

6. 6.04 ◯ 6.44

6. Which is less? 04 or 44

7. 8.01 ◯ 8.001

8. 5.4 ◯ 3.6

9. 4.9 ◯ 6.02

10. 4.50 ◯ 4.5

Order from least to greatest.

11. 9.1, 9.001, 9.011

12. 1.25, 1.205, 1.025

_____

_____

11. How many zeros do you add to 9.1? 0, 1, or 2

13. $7\frac{1}{2}$, $7\frac{2}{3}$, $7\frac{1}{3}$

14. 5, $4\frac{9}{10}$, $4\frac{7}{8}$

_____

_____

Solve.

15. Holly's bracelets are $7\frac{1}{2}$ inches, $7\frac{1}{4}$ inches, and $7\frac{3}{8}$ inches long. Which bracelet is the longest?

16. The fastest times for the Olympic 100-meter race were 9.86, 9.87, and 9.85 seconds. Which time was the fastest?

15. What is the least common denominator? 2, 4, or 8

_____

_____

On Your Own!

Circle the answer for each question.

For Questions 1–4, choose the symbol that goes in the blank to make the sentence true.

1. $\frac{5}{8}$ ____ $\frac{3}{5}$

   A.   <
   B.   >
   C.   =
   D.   ×

2. $4\frac{8}{12}$ ____ $4\frac{6}{9}$

   A.   <
   B.   >
   C.   =
   D.   ×

3. 10.2 ____ 9.9

   A.   <
   B.   >
   C.   =
   D.   ×

4. 6.009 ____ 6.03

   A.   <
   B.   >
   C.   =
   D.   ×

5. Loni measured a countertop four times and got these four measurements. Which is the least?

   A.   2.4 m
   B.   2.39 m
   C.   2.401 m
   D.   2.385 m

6. Daniel is choosing a walking stick from the lengths shown below. Which is the longest?

   A. $4\frac{3}{8}$ feet   C. $4\frac{3}{4}$ feet

   B. $4\frac{1}{2}$ feet   D. $4\frac{2}{3}$ feet

7. Which of these numbers has a value between 80.003 and 80.03?

   A.   80.1
   B.   80.029
   C.   80.033
   D.   80.2

8. Which is ordered from least to greatest?

   A. $5\frac{3}{10}, 5\frac{3}{8}, 5\frac{1}{2}$

   B. $5\frac{1}{2}, 5\frac{3}{10}, 5\frac{3}{8}$

   C. $5\frac{3}{10}, 5\frac{1}{2}, 5\frac{3}{8}$

   D. $5\frac{1}{2}, 5\frac{3}{8}, 5\frac{3}{10}$

9.   **Below are the masses of 4 puppies.**

   11.08 kg   10.9 kg   11.4 kg   11.245 kg

   Part A   Order the masses from least to greatest.

   _____ _____ _____ _____

   Part B   Explain how you ordered the masses in Part A.

   _____

   _____

   _____

   _____

 Draw a line to match each symbol to its meaning.

10.   <   multiply

11.   =   is less than

12.   >   is equal to

13.   ×   is greater than

LESSON 9 Using Operations to Solve Problems

Review It!   When you solve problems, remember this word:

reciprocal two numbers that have a product of 1

$\frac{1}{10}$ is the reciprocal of $\frac{10}{1}$ because $\frac{1}{10} \times \frac{10}{1} = 1$

Divide. $8\frac{3}{4} \div 5$

Step 1   Rename both numbers as improper fractions.

$8\frac{3}{4} = \frac{35}{4}$

$5 = \frac{5}{1}$

Step 2   Rewrite the division problem as a multiplication problem.
Multiply the first fraction by the reciprocal of the second fraction.

$\frac{35}{4} \div \frac{5}{1} = \frac{35}{4} \times \frac{1}{5}$ ◄ ···

> **REMEMBER** To write the reciprocal, switch the numbers in the numerator and denominator.

Step 3   Multiply the two fractions.

$\frac{35}{4} \times \frac{1}{5} = \frac{35 \times 1}{4 \times 5} = \frac{35}{20}$

Step 4   Rename the improper fraction as a mixed number in simplest form.

$\frac{35}{20} = 1\frac{15}{20} = 1\frac{\boxed{}}{\boxed{}}$

So, $8\frac{3}{4} \div 5 = $ _____.

Try It! Compute.

1. $\frac{3}{4} + \frac{5}{8}$

2. $\frac{5}{8} \times \frac{4}{5}$

3. $6\frac{1}{2} - 2\frac{2}{3}$

_____ _____ _____

4. $3\frac{1}{3} + 4\frac{7}{8}$

5. $3\frac{1}{2} \times \frac{5}{7}$

6. $5\frac{1}{3} \div \frac{5}{6}$

_____ _____ _____

7. $3.45 + 7.1$

8. $2.9 + 0.88$

9. $4.63 - 2.901$

_____ _____ _____

10. 5.6×4.5

11. 2.01×7.44

12. $5.3 \div 0.25$

_____ _____ _____

Solve.

13. If 1 foot is $\frac{1}{3}$ yard, how many yards is 10 feet?

_____

14. Jason jumped 1.89 meters, and Peggy jumped 1.9 meters in the long jump. How much farther did Peggy jump than Jason?

_____

Ask Yourself

1.
Which operations require a common denominator?
add, subtract, multiply, divide

2.
Do you multiply the numerators, denominators, or both?

7.
For which operations do you align the decimal?
add, subtract, multiply, divide

13.
Which operation is needed?
addition or multiplication

On Your Own!

Circle the answer for each question.

1. Divide. $1\frac{3}{5} \div \frac{4}{5}$

   A. $\frac{1}{2}$

   B. $\frac{25}{32}$

   C. $1\frac{7}{25}$

   D. 2

2. Subtract. $8 - 3.45$

   A. 4.45

   B. 4.55

   C. 5.45

   D. 5.55

3. Multiply. 5.02×2.8

   A. 10.456

   B. 14.056

   C. 14.56

   D. 50.56

4. Add. $5\frac{2}{3} + 4\frac{5}{6}$

   A. $9\frac{1}{6}$

   B. $9\frac{1}{2}$

   C. $9\frac{3}{4}$

   D. $10\frac{1}{2}$

5. Jorge bought $7\frac{3}{4}$ pounds of apples and $11\frac{5}{8}$ pounds of oranges. How much more did the oranges weigh than the apples?

   A. $3\frac{7}{8}$

   B. $4\frac{1}{8}$

   C. $4\frac{1}{2}$

   D. $19\frac{3}{8}$

6. Tina buys 6 cinema tickets for $6.75 each. She gives the cashier three $20 bills. How much change should she receive?

   A. $7.25

   B. $13.25

   C. $19.50

   D. $20.50

7. Lois says that $\frac{2}{3}$ of the students in her class are boys. There are 24 students in her class. How many are **girls**?

   A. 4

   B. 8

   C. 12

   D. 16

8. Pennsylvania has 51 miles of coast along Lake Erie and 57 miles of shoreline along the Delaware Estuary. The total distance around Pennsylvania is about 1,000 miles.

Part A How much of that distance around Pennsylvania is **not** shoreline?

_____

Part B Explain how you found your answer.

_____

_____

_____

Math Words **Draw a line to match each symbol to its meaning.**

9. −   add

10. ×   divide

11. =   equals

12. ÷   multiply

13. +   subtract

LESSON 10 Solving Problems with Estimation

Review It!

When you estimate solutions, remember these words:

estimate a reasonable guess at the correct answer to a problem

compatible numbers numbers that are easy to compute mentally

Example 1 **Round to estimate $18.23 + $3.67.**

Step 1 $18.23 rounded to the nearest dollar is $18.

Step 2 $3.67 rounded to the nearest dollar is $4.

Step 3 Add the two rounded numbers. $18 + $4 = _____

So, a good estimate of $18.23 + $3.67 is _____.

Example 2 **Use compatible numbers to estimate 5.822 ÷ 8.2.**

Step 1 Find compatible numbers that are close to 5.822 and 8.2.

- Round 8.2 to 8.

- Find a number close to 5.822 that is divisible by 8.
  5.6 is a good choice. ◄·····················

Step 2 Divide. 5.6 ÷ 8 = _____

So, a good estimate of 5.822 ÷ 8.2 is about _____.

> **REMEMBER** You can use a known fact, 56 ÷ 8, to help you estimate.

Estimate each answer.

Ask Yourself

1. $8.12 + $3.56

2. 2.8 + 9.1 + 11.35

_____

1.
Which gives the best estimate?
8 + 3, 8 + 4,
or 9 + 4

3. $122.58 − $25.19

4. 397.01 − 123.79

_____

5. 61.3 × 5.9

6. $4.89 × 10.25

_____

7. 369.38 ÷ 80.3

8. 26.78 ÷ 6.5

_____

7.
Which number is most compatible with 80?
340, 360, 380,
or 400

9. 24.9 × 7.8

10. 12 + 19 + 55 + 4

_____

Estimate to solve.

11. A wagon holds 4 boxes that weigh 58.2 pounds, 17.9 pounds, 23.4 pounds, and 51.5 pounds. About how much weight is the wagon holding?

_____

11.
To which place will you round each number so you can add mentally?
ones place or tens place

12. Glenda gave a $10 bill to the cashier for an $8.26 lunch tab. About how much change should she receive?

_____

On Your Own!

Circle the answer for each question.

1. An 8.4-ounce bottle of hand lotion costs $9.89. Which is the best estimate of the price per ounce?

   A. $0.80

   B. $0.90

   C. $1.00

   D. $1.10

2. Mr. Hass is ordering 22 books for his reading class. Each book costs $17.70. Which is the best estimate of how much he will pay for the books?

   A. $200

   B. $300

   C. $400

   D. $600

3. A vacationing family drove 138.2 miles on Monday, 217.9 miles on Tuesday, 58.0 miles on Wednesday, and 261.7 miles on Thursday. Which is the best estimate of the distance they drove on the four days altogether?

   A. 500 miles

   B. 700 miles

   C. 800 miles

   D. 1,000 miles

4. Curtain material costs $68.99 per yard. Helena needs 48 yards. Which is the best estimate for how much the material will cost?

   A. $2,400

   B. $2,800

   C. $3,000

   D. $3,500

5. Danielle saves $110 from her paycheck each month. Which is the best estimate for how much she can save in 18 months?

   A. $1,000

   B. $2,000

   C. $3,000

   D. $4,000

6. Phil went shopping with $96.44. He spent 41.55. Which is the best estimate for how much money he had left?

   A. $45

   B. $55

   C. $65

   D. $140

7.   David reasoned that if 12 ounces of bath oil costs $21.60, then 1 ounce costs $0.18.

Part A   Without solving, explain why you think David's reasoning is wrong.

_____

_____

_____

Part B   Use what you know about estimation to provide a reasonable estimate for $21.60 ÷ 12.

_____

 Math Words   **Draw a line to match each word to its meaning.**

8.   estimate   numbers that are easy to compute mentally

9.   compatible numbers   an answer that is reasonably close to an exact answer

10.   round   to replace an exact number with another that is close to its value

Review It! When you study elapsed time, remember this word:

elapsed time the amount of time that passes from the start to the end of an event

5:00–6:15 ◄················· The elapsed time is 1 hr 15 min.

A show begins at 7:45 P.M. and ends at 10:10 P.M. How long did the show last?

Step 1 Count forward the hours from 7:45.

7:45 to 8:45 equals 1 hour.

8:45 to 9:45 equals 1 hour. ◄·······

In all, that equals _____ hours.

> **THINK** Don't count up to 10:45 since that's past 10:10.

Step 2 Count forward the minutes from 9:45.

9:45 to 10:00 makes 15 minutes. ◄·······

10:00 to 10:10 makes 10 more minutes.

In all, that equals _____ minutes.

> **THINK** Count up to whole hours. Then count on to minutes after the hour.

So, the show lasted _____ hours _____ minutes.

Find the elapsed time.

1. start: 3:30 P.M. **2.** start: 2:15 P.M. **3.** start: 8:10 A.M.
     end: 6:00 P.M.   end: 9:35 P.M.   end: 10:55 A.M.

_____ _____ _____

4. start: 1:30 P.M. **5.** start: 6:45 A.M. **6.** start: 10:40 A.M.
     end: 5:15 P.M.   end: 11:25 A.M.   end: 6:30 P.M.

_____ _____ _____

Solve.

7. A football game began at 11:10 A.M. and ended at 1:40 P.M. How long did the game last?

_____

8. Maria's gardening class begins at 8:00 A.M. and ends at 11:15 A.M. How long is Maria's gardening class?

_____

9. Tom went walking for 2 hours 15 minutes today. He started his walk at 8:50 A.M. When did Tom finish his walk?

_____

10. It started hailing in Congers at 11:15 A.M. this morning and didn't stop for 90 minutes. What time was it when it stopped hailing?

_____

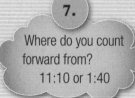

Ask Yourself

1.
How many whole hours do you count? 1, 2, or 3

7.
Where do you count forward from? 11:10 or 1:40

Measurement

Circle the answer for each question.

1. A class begins at 10:05 A.M. and ends at 10:50 A.M. How long is the class?

    A. 45 minutes

    B. 55 minutes

    C. 1 hour 45 minutes

    D. 1 hour 55 minutes

2. Jasper started cooking dinner at 3:15 P.M. and didn't finish cooking until 6:00 P.M. How long did it take Jasper to cook dinner?

    A. 2 hr 15 min

    B. 2 hr 45 min

    C. 3 hr 15 min

    D. 3 hr 45 min

3. On Saturday, the Watertown library opens at 9:00 A.M. and closes at 3:30 P.M. How long is the library open?

    A. 3 hr 30 min

    B. 4 hr 30 min

    C. 5 hr 30 min

    D. 6 hr 30 min

4. Chase started a marathon at 8:35 A.M. and finished the race at 11:25 A.M. How long did it take Chase to complete the marathon?

    A. 2 hr 10 min

    B. 2 hr 50 min

    C. 3 hr 10 min

    D. 3 hr 50 min

5. A movie started at 8:15 P.M. and lasted 100 minutes. At what time did the movie end?

    A. 9:15 P.M.

    B. 9:40 P.M.

    C. 9:55 P.M.

    D. 10:15 P.M.

6. It took Ami 5 hours 30 minutes to drive to her brother's cabin. If she started driving at 10:20 A.M., when did Ami reach the cabin?

    A. 3:50 A.M.

    B. 3:50 P.M.

    C. 5:50 A.M.

    D. 5:50 P.M.

Grace begins work at 8:30 A.M. and finishes at 5:15 P.M. each day. Use this information for Questions 7 and 8.

7. How long does Grace work each day?

    _____

8. Show how you found your answer for Question 7.

    _____

    _____

    _____

 Fill in the blanks.

9. The amount of time that passes from the start to the end of an event

    is called _____ _____.

10. In 1 hour there are _____ minutes.

11. The hours between midnight and noon use the abbreviation _____.

12. The hours between noon and midnight use the abbreviation _____.

Measurement

Review It! When you measure with an inch ruler, remember how to read the marks on an inch ruler:

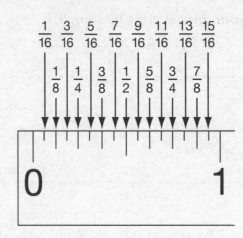

Measure the length of this craft stick to the nearest $\frac{1}{16}$ inch.

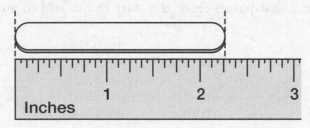

Inches

Step 1 Notice the zero mark on the ruler lines up with one end of the craft stick.

Find where the ruler and craft stick line up at the other end.

The craft stick is more than 2 inches, but less than 3 inches, long.

Step 2 The craft stick is 4 marks past the 2-inch mark on the ruler.

That mark measures $\frac{4}{16}$ inch.

Step 3 Simplify the fraction. $\frac{4}{16} =$ _____

> **REMEMBER** The measure is greater than 2.

So, the craft stick is _____ inches long. ◄······································

Measurement

Try It! Measure to the nearest $\frac{1}{16}$ inch. Simplify the fraction, if necessary.

Ask Yourself

1. _____

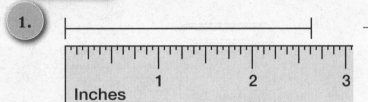

1.

What is the whole-number part of the answer?
1, 2, or 3

2. _____

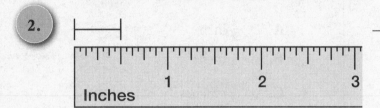

2.

Which will the answer be?
whole number
fraction
mixed number

3. _____

4. _____

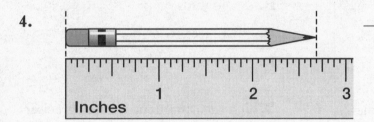

Which is the smaller unit?
eighth or sixteenth

5. _____

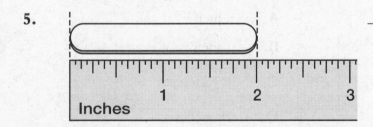

Circle the more precise measurement.

6. $\frac{7}{16}$ inch
$\frac{7}{8}$ inch

7. 4 miles
$3\frac{1}{2}$ mile

8. 9 inches
9 feet

9. 2.4 cm
3.8 mm

10. 0.8 km
10 cm

11. 6 feet
2 yards

Measurement

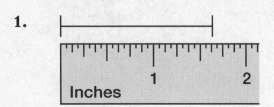

On Your Own!

Circle the answer for each question.

Measure each to the nearest $\frac{1}{16}$ inch.

1.

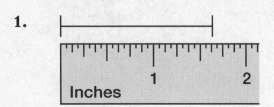

A. $\frac{5}{8}$ inch

B. $\frac{5}{16}$ inch

C. $1\frac{5}{8}$ inches

D. $1\frac{5}{16}$ inches

2.

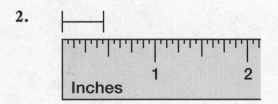

A. $\frac{7}{16}$ inch   C. $1\frac{7}{16}$ inches

B. $\frac{7}{8}$ inch   D. $1\frac{7}{8}$ inches

3.

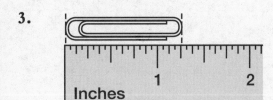

A. $1\frac{1}{16}$ inches   C. $1\frac{1}{4}$ inches

B. $1\frac{1}{8}$ inches   D. $2\frac{1}{4}$ inches

4.

A. $\frac{1}{2}$ inch

B. 1 inch

C. $1\frac{1}{2}$ inches

D. 2 inches

5. Which measurement is most precise?

A. $\frac{1}{8}$ mile

B. 40 yards

C. 12 feet

D. 89 inches

6. Which measurement is most precise?

A. $\frac{1}{2}$ inch

B. 1 inch

C. $1\frac{9}{16}$ inches

D. $1\frac{3}{4}$ inches

7. Which measurement is most precise?

A. 220 mm

B. 22 cm

C. 2.2 m

D. 2 km

Measurement

8. Place a mark at $3\frac{3}{4}$ inches. Label it A.

9. Explain how you correctly placed your mark in Question 9.

_____

_____

_____

_____

Math Words

Order the lengths from least precise to most precise.

eighth   fourth   half   sixteenth

10. _____, _____, _____, _____.

Measurement

13 Measuring Angles

Review It! When you describe angles, remember these words:

vertex the "corner" of an angle

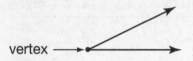

vertex ⟶

right angle an angle that measures exactly 90°

acute angle an angle that measures between 0° and 90°

obtuse angle an angle that measures between 90° and 180°

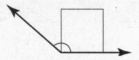

What is the measure of angle *PQR*?

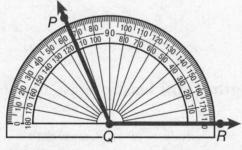

Step 1 Decide which scale to use.

Use the scale that starts with 0° on the right side.

Step 2 Classify the angle.

The angle is greater than 90°, so it is an _____ angle.

Step 3 Measure the angle.

The angle is _____°.

So, the measure of the angle is _____.

Measurement

Try It! Classify the angle as acute, right, or obtuse. Then tell if its measure is closest to 0°, 90°, or 180°.

1.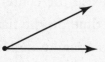

_____

_____

2.

_____

_____

1.

Which is the smaller angle?
acute or obtuse

3.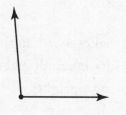

_____

_____

4.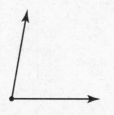

_____

_____

5.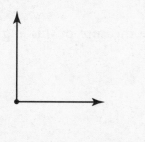

_____

_____

6.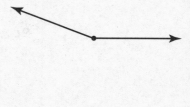

_____

_____

Solve.

7. A leaning fence post makes a 25° angle with the ground. How many degrees is it off from being upright?

7.

What angle measure does an upright post make?
0°, 90°, or 180°

_____

Circle the answer for each question.

Use this figure for Questions 1–3.

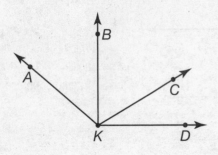

1. Which angle is a right angle?

   A. angle *AKC*

   B. angle *AKD*

   C. angle *BKD*

   D. angle *CKD*

2. Which angle is an obtuse angle?

   A. angle *AKC*

   B. angle *BKC*

   C. angle *BKD*

   D. angle *CKD*

3. Which angle measures less than angle *AKB*?

   A. angle *AKC*

   B. angle *BKC*

   C. angle *BKD*

   D. angle *CKD*

4. The hands on a clock form angles that have a vertex at the center of a clock. At which time do the hands of the clock form a straight angle?

   A. 9:00

   B. 6:00

   C. 3:20

   D. 1:30

5. A leaning tree makes a 70° angle with ground. How many degrees is it off from being upright?

   A. 0°

   B. 20°

   C. 30°

   D. 70°

6. Estimate the measure of this angle.

   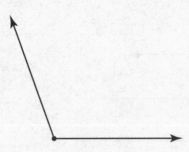

   A. 70°

   B. 90°

   C. 110°

   D. 160°

Use this angle to answer Questions 7 and 8.

7. Use a protractor to measure the angle. What is the measure of the angle?

_____

8. Classify the angle. Compare its measure to the measure of a right angle.

_____

_____

_____

 Fill in the blanks.

9. The point where an angle's sides meet is the _____.

10. A(n) _____ is formed by two rays that share an endpoint.

11. An angle that measures exactly 90° is a(n) _____ angle.

12. An angle that measures more than 90° is a(n) _____ angle.

13. An angle that measures less than 90° is a(n) _____ angle.

14. An angle that measures exactly 180° is a(n) _____ angle.

Measurement

When you find the distance around a figure, remember these words:

perimeter distance around a polygon found by adding the lengths of its sides

polygon a figure made with line segments that enclose a space

regular polygon a polygon with equal sides and equal angles

irregular polygon any polygon that is not regular

In Sullivan County Pennsylvania there is a house shaped like an octagon. Each side of the Octagon House is 16 feet long. What is the perimeter of the Octagon?

16 ft

Octagon House

Step 1 Find what you know about the Octagon House.

An octagon has 8 sides.

Each side of the house is the same length.

Each side is _____ feet long.

Step 2 Find the perimeter. ◂···

16 × _____ = _____

> **THINK** If all the sides are equal, multiply.

So, the perimeter of the Octagon House is _____ feet.

Try It!   Find the perimeter of the figure.

Ask Yourself

1.

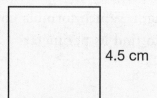

4.5 cm

_____

2.

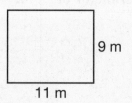

9 m

11 m

_____

1.

How many equal sides does a square have?

2 or 4

3.

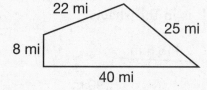

22 mi

25 mi

8 mi

40 mi

_____

4.

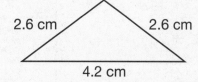

2.6 cm   2.6 cm

4.2 cm

_____

5.

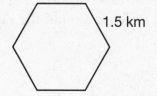

1.5 km

_____

6.

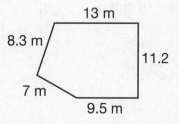

13 m

8.3 m

11.2

7 m

9.5 m

_____

Solve.

7. Kathryn wants to fence in her rectangular backyard. Her yard is 50 yards wide and 100 yards long. How much fencing does she need?

_____

8. A square window is 124 centimeters on each side. Arnie is painting around the edge of the window. How many centimeters will Arnie paint?

_____

7.

How many sides of her yard measure 50 yards?

1 or 2

Circle the answer for each question.

1. Tonya wants to find the perimeter of this rectangle.

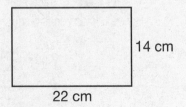

14 cm

22 cm

   Which expression should she **not** use?

   A. 14 + 14 + 22 + 22

   B. 2 × 14 + 2 × 22

   C. 2 × (14 + 22)

   D. 2 + 14 +2 + 22

2. What is the perimeter of this irregular pentagon?

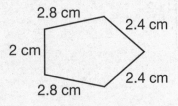

2.8 cm

2.4 cm

2 cm

2.4 cm

2.8 cm

   A. 10.4 cm   **C.** 12.4 cm

   B. 10.6 cm   **D.** 12.6 cm

3. One half of a volleyball court is a square. One side is 30 feet. What is the perimeter of half a court?

   A. 60 feet   **C.** 120 feet

   B. 90 feet   **D.** 150 feet

4. A regular octagon has 8 sides of equal length. Which formula could you use to find its perimeter?

   A. $P = 8s$

   B. $P = 2 \times 8s$

   C. $P = 2 \times 8s + 2 \times 8s$

   D. $P = s + 8$

5. A park is in this shape.

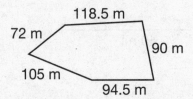

118.5 m

72 m

90 m

105 m

94.5 m

   The city wants to fence it in. How many feet of fence should the city order?

   A. 239.7 m

   B. 480 m

   C. 2,397 m

   D. 4,800 m

6. The perimeter of a rectangle is 50 inches. If its width is 11 inches, what is its length?

   A. 14 inches

   B. 28 inches

   C. 36 inches

   D. 39 inches

7. The perimeter of a square is 64 yards.

Part A What is the length of one side?

_____

Part B Explain how you know your answer to Part A is correct.

_____

_____

_____

 Fill in the blanks.

8. A _____ is formed by line segments and it completely encloses a space.

9. A(n) _____ polygon has equal sides and angles.

10. A(n) _____ polygon can have equal sides but unequal angles.

11. The _____ of a polygon is found by adding the lengths of all its sides.

Measurement

Review It!

When you classify triangles, remember these words:

Triangles named for their sides			Triangles named for their largest angle		
equilateral	isosceles	scalene	acute	right	obtuse
3 equal sides	2 equal sides	0 equal sides	3 acute angles	1 right angle 2 acute angles	1 obtuse and 2 acute angles

leg one of the two shorter sides of a right triangle

hypotenuse the longest side of a right triangle, located across from the right angle

Classify triangle *ABC* according to its sides and angles.

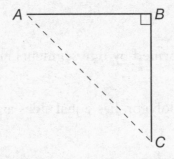

Step 1 Look at the sides.

$\overline{AB}$ and $\overline{BC}$ are the same length. ◄••••••••••••••••••

> **REMEMBER** You can use a sheet of paper to compare the sides.

A triangle with two equal sides is _____.

Step 2 Look at the angles.

$\angle B$ is a right angle.

$\angle A$ and $\angle C$ are acute angles.

A triangle with one right angle and two acute angles is _____.

So, triangle *ABC* is a(n) _____ _____ **triangle.**

Geometry

Classify each triangle using its sides and angles.

1.

_____

2.

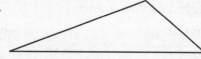

_____

1.

How many equal sides does it have? 0, 2, or 3

3.

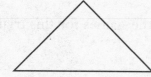

_____

4.

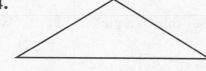

_____

5.

_____

6.

_____

Use this figure to answer Questions 7 and 8.

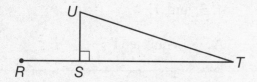

7. Which segment name the hypotenuse of a right triangle?

_____

8. Which segments name the legs of a right triangle?

_____ and _____

7.

Where is the longest side? opposite a right angle next to a right angle

Geometry

On Your Own! Circle the answer for each question.

1. Which type of triangle has two acute angles and one obtuse angle?

   A. acute

   B. obtuse

   C. right

   D. equilateral

2. Which name describes this triangle?

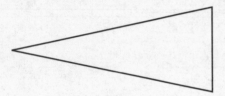

   A. obtuse

   B. scalene

   C. equilateral

   D. isosceles

3. Which line segment is the hypotenuse of a right triangle?

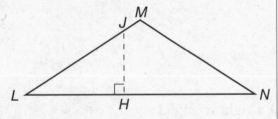

   A. $\overline{JH}$

   B. $\overline{JL}$

   C. $\overline{LN}$

   D. $\overline{MN}$

4. What is the name for a triangle that has no sides equal in length?

   A. scalene

   B. isosceles

   C. right

   D. equilateral

5. What are the names for this triangle?

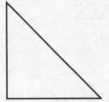

   A. isosceles and right

   B. scalene and right

   C. equilateral and obtuse

   D. hypotenuse and right

6. Which word **best** describes a triangle that has sides with lengths 4, 5, and 7?

   A. equilateral

   B. isosceles

   C. scalene

   D. right

Geometry

7.   Use rectangle *ABCD* below to answer the questions.

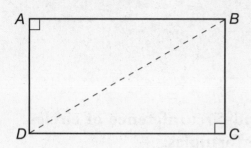

Part A   Are the triangles formed by diagonal $\overline{BD}$ scalene, isosceles, or equilateral?

_____

Part B   Are the triangles formed by diagonal $\overline{BD}$ right, obtuse, or acute?

_____

 Fill in the blanks.

8.   A triangle with two acute and one right angle is a(n) _____ triangle.

9.   A right triangle has two _____ and one _____ for sides.

10.   A triangle with one obtuse angle and no equal sides is a(n) _____
_____ triangle.

11.   A triangle with equal sides is a(n) _____ triangle.

12.   In a right triangle the _____ is the longest side.

LESSON 16 ▶ Circles

When you find area and circumference of circles, remember these circle formulas:

Player	Formula
Diameter	$d = 2r$
Radius	$r = \frac{d}{2}$
Circumference (using diameter)	$C = \pi d$
Circumference (using radius)	$C = 2\pi r$
Area (using radius)	$A = \pi r^2$

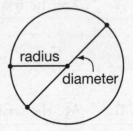

In these formulas, r = radius, d = diameter,
C = circumference (distance around), A = area.

Find the area of the circle. Use $\frac{22}{7}$ for π.

28 cm

Step 1 Decide which formula to use.
$A = \pi r^2$

Step 2 Find the radius of the circle. _____
The radius is 14 cm.

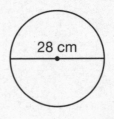
REMEMBER The radius is half the diameter.

Step 3 Substitute the values of r and π into the formula.
Then find the area.

$A = \pi r^2$ **REMEMBER** $r^2 = r \times r$.

$A = \frac{22}{7} \times 14^2$

$A = \frac{22}{7} \times \underline{\hspace{1cm}}$

$A = \underline{\hspace{1cm}}$

So, the area of the circle is _____ cm^2.

Find the circumference of the circle with the given measure. Use $\frac{22}{7}$ for π.

1. radius = 7 meters

2. diameter = 42 inches

_____

_____

3. diameter = 7 miles

4. radius = 14 feet

_____

_____

5. radius = 70 centimeters

6. diameter = 2 yards

_____

_____

Find the area of the circle with the given measure. Use 3.14 for π.

7. diameter = 6 yards

8. radius = 4.5 centimeters

_____

_____

9. radius = 0.5 feet

10. diameter = 20 miles

_____

_____

11. radius = 8.5 kilometers

12. diameter = 11 inches

_____

_____

1.

Which formula
should you use?
$C = \pi d$
$C = 2\pi r$

7.

What is the radius
of the circle?
3 yards or 12 yards

Geometry

Circle the answer for each question.

1. The diameter of a circle is 8.2 cm. What is its radius?

   A. 4.1 cm

   B. 8.2 cm

   C. 16.4 cm

   D. 16.81 cm

2. The radius of a circle is 50 centimeters. Calculate the circumference of the circle. Use 3.14 for π.

   A. 78.5 centimeters

   B. 157 centimeters

   C. 314 centimeters

   D. 7,850 centimeters

3. Find the area of a circle with a 70-inch diameter. Use $\frac{22}{7}$ for π.

   A. 110 inches

   B. 220 inches

   C. 440 inches

   D. 3,850 inches

4. Find the area of a circle with radius 40 feet. Use 3.14 for π.

   A. 125.6 ft^2

   B. 251.2 ft^2

   C. 1,256 ft^2

   D. 5,024 ft^2

5. The diameter of a circle is 12 kilometers. What is the area of the circle? Leave your answer in terms of π.

   A. 24π km^2

   B. 36π km^2

   C. 144π km^2

   D. 576π km^2

6. The circumference of a circle is 33 meters. Find the diameter. Use $\frac{22}{7}$ for π.

   A. 5.25 meters   C. 17.5 meters

   B. 10.5 meters   D. 21 meters

7. The circumference of a circle is 785 yards. Find the radius. Use 3.14 for π.

   A. 125 yards   C. 392.5 yards

   B. 250 yards   D. 500 yards

8. The circumference of a circle is 4π cm. What is its area? Leave your answer in terms of π.

   A. 2π cm^2

   B. 4π cm^2

   C. 9π cm^2

   D. 16π cm^2

9. Jim used 3 as a value of π to estimate the circumference of a circular wheel that had a radius of 15 inches.

   Part A   What was Jim's estimate?

   _____

   Part B   Use what you know about finding the circumference of a circle to explain your answer.

   _____

   _____

   _____

 Draw a line to match each word to its meaning.

10.   circumference   a round figure

11.   diameter   a line segment that passes through the center of a circle and whose endpoints are both on the circle

12.   radius   a line segment with one endpoint at the center of the circle and the other on the circle

13.   circle   perimeter of a circle

Geometry

When you identify polygons, remember these words:

parallel sides sides that are always the same distance apart

quadrilateral any polygon with 4 sides

parallelogram a quadrilateral with opposite sides parallel and equal in length

rectangle a parallelogram with 4 right angles

rhombus a parallelogram with 4 equal sides

square a parallelogram with 4 right angles and 4 equal sides

trapezoid a quadrilateral with just one pair of parallel sides

Geometry

Write all possible names for the figure.

Step 1 Look at the figure.

It is an enclosed figure with no curves, so it is a polygon. ◄ ·······················

REMEMBER All closed figures with line segments for sides are polygons.

Step 2 Look at the sides.

It has 4 sides, so it is a quadrilateral.

It has 2 pairs of parallel sides, so it is a parallelogram.

Step 3 Look at the angles.

The figure has all right angles, so it is a square or rectangle.

But, this figure cannot be a square because its sides are not equal.

So, all possible names for the figure are _____, _____,

and _____, _____.

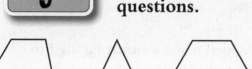 **Use these figures to answer the questions.**

 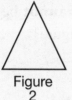

Figure
1

Figure
2

Figure
3

Figure
4

Figure
5

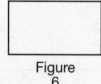 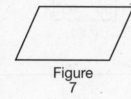 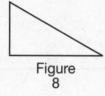

Figure
6

Figure
7

Figure
8

Figure
9

1. Which figures are quadrilaterals? ____, ____, ____, ____, ____

2. Are any of the figures **not** polygons? ____

3. Which figures are parallelograms? ____, ____, ____, ____

4. Which figures are regular? ____, ____, ____

5. Which figures are rectangles? ____, ____

6. Which quadrilateral is **not** a parallelogram? ____

7. Name the figure identified in Question 6. _____

8. Which figures are triangles? ____, ____

9. What are all possible names for Figure 4? _____,

_____, _____, and _____

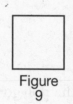
Geometry

Circle the answer for each question.

1. Which of these is a regular quadrilateral?

   A. equilateral triangle

   B. parallelogram

   C. rhombus

   D. square

2. Which describes the polygon shown below?

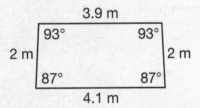

   A. rectangle

   B. trapezoid

   C. parallelogram

   D. rhombus

3. Which statement is **not** true?

   A. All rhombuses are rectangles.

   B. All rectangles are parallelograms.

   C. All trapezoids are polygons.

   D. All squares are polygons.

4. Which name **cannot** be used to describe this figure?

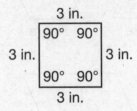

   A. square

   B. rhombus

   C. trapezoid

   D. rectangle

5. Carmen drew two equilateral triangles and put them together in the figure below.

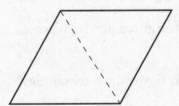

   Which **best** describes the new shape?

   A. trapezoid

   B. rhombus

   C. square

   D. rectangle

6. What do a rhombus and rectangle have in common?

_____

_____

7. A figure has four sides and no right angles. List all possible names for the figure.

_____ , _____ , _____ , _____ , _____

Math Words   **Fill in the blanks.**

8. Two sides of a polygon are _____ if they are always the same distance apart.

9. If a polygon has four sides, it is a _____ .

10. A quadrilateral with just one pair of parallel sides is a _____ .

11. A quadrilateral that is both a rhombus and a rectangle is a _____ .

12. A quadrilateral that is a rhombus is a special type of _____ .

Number of Degrees in Triangles, Quadrilaterals, and Circles

Review It! When you find angle measures, remember these angle sums:

- The sum of the angle measures in a **triangle** is 180°.
- The sum of the angle measures in a **quadrilateral** is 360°.
- There are 360° in a **circle**.

This drawing shows plans for a dog pen. What will be the angle measure at the fourth corner?

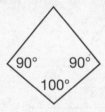

Step 1 Identify the figure. ◄ ·

> **THINK** Identify the figure to find out the sum of all the angles.

The figure has 4 sides, so it is a quadrilateral.

Step 2 Find the sum of the angle measures in a quadrilateral.

The sum of the angle measures is 360°.

Step 3 Find the sum of the angle measures you know about.

100° + 90° + 90° = _____°

Step 4 Subtract.

360° − _____° = _____°

So, the measure of the missing angle is _____.

Geometry

Find the missing angle measure shown by the question mark (?).

1.

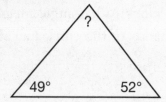

49°   52°

_____

2.

?

_____

3.

130°

?

_____

4.

68°   112°

?   68°

_____

Solve.

5. Mandy measured two angles of a rhombus. They are both 50°. What is the sum of the measures of the other two angles?

_____

6. Theo measured two angles of a triangle. Both angles measure 24°. What is the measure of the third angle?

_____

Ask Yourself

1.
How many degrees are in a triangle?
180 or 360

2.
How many degrees are in a circle?
180 or 360

5.
What is a rhombus?
triangle
quadrilateral
circle

Geometry

Circle the answer for each question.

1. What is the missing angle measure in this triangle?

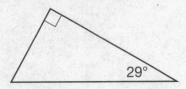

   A.   61°
   B.   79°
   C.   81°
   D.   119°

2. The two missing angles in the parallelogram have equal measure. What is the measure of one of them?

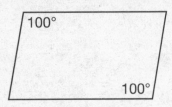

   A.   50°
   B.   80°
   C.   100°
   D.   160°

3. It is 9 o'clock. What angle measure do the hands of the clock make?

   A.   0°
   B.   90°
   C.   100°
   D.   180°

4. How many degrees are in a semicircle?

   A.   25°
   B.   50°
   C.   90°
   D.   180°

5. What is the measure of the missing angle?

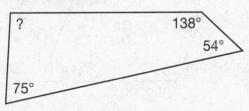

   A.   33°
   B.   90°
   C.   93°
   D.   117°

Geometry

6. Three angles of a trapezoid are 22°, 46°, and 134°. Explain how you can find the measure of the other angle.

_____

_____

_____

_____

Math Words **Tell what the sum of the angle measures are for each figure.**

7. quarter circle _____

8. obtuse isosceles triangle _____

9. trapezoid _____

10. square _____

11. equilateral triangle _____

12. right scalene triangle _____

13. parallelogram _____

14. semicircle _____

Geometry

Points, Segments, Lines, Angles, and Planes

Geometry

Review It! When you describe geometric figures, remember these words:

line one straight string of points that extends forever in both directions

line segment part of a line between two endpoints

plane a set of points that form a flat surface

intersecting lines two or more lines that meet at a point

parallel (∥) lines two or more lines in one plane that never intersect

perpendicular (⊥) lines two lines that intersect to form right angles

---

Name a fourth point in the same plane as points A, E, and H.

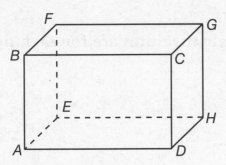

Step 1 Locate the plane.

Is it front, back, top, bottom, left, or right? _____ ◄····

> **THINK** All three points must be on the same surface.

Step 2 Name all the points in that plane. _____, _____, _____, _____

Step 3 Which point is not included in the original list? _____

So, a fourth point in the same plane as points A, E, and H is point _____.

Use the diagram to answer Questions 1–3.

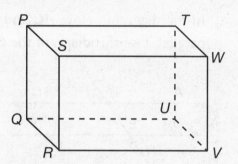

1. Name three line segments parallel to $\overline{PQ}$. ____, ____, ____

2. Name two line segments perpendicular to $\overline{QU}$. ____, ____

3. Name a fourth point in the same plane as points P, T,

   and U. ____

Use the diagram to answer Questions 4–6.

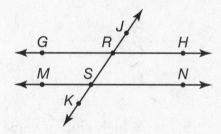

4. Name four acute angles. _____, _____,

   _____, _____

5. Name a line parallel to $\overline{MN}$. ____

6. Name two segments with endpoint H. _____

1.

Parallel lines _____, intersect
do not intersect

4.

What is the measure
of an acute angle?
between 0° and 90°
between 90° and
180°

Geometry

Circle the answer for each question.

1. Which **best** describes this figure?

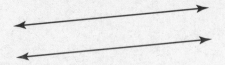

   A. parallel line segments

   B. parallel lines

   C. perpendicular lines

   D. intersecting lines that are not perpendicular

2. Which line segment is **not** in a plane with $\overline{MN}$?

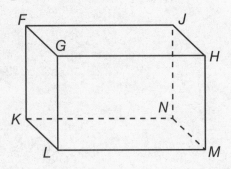

   A. $\overline{KL}$

   B. $\overline{JH}$

   C. $\overline{HM}$

   D. $\overline{GH}$

In the diagram below, $\overline{AC}$ and $\overline{DF}$ are parallel. Use this diagram for Questions 3–5.

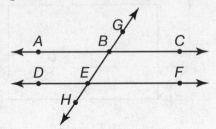

3. Which kind of angle is $\angle GBE$?

   A. acute

   B. obtuse

   C. right

   D. straight

4. Which kind of angle is $\angle ABE$?

   A. acute

   B. obtuse

   C. right

   D. straight

5. Which kind of angle is $\angle HEF$?

   A. acute

   B. obtuse

   C. right

   D. straight

Geometry

6. Describe the angles formed by perpendicular lines.

_____

7. Describe the angles formed by intersecting lines that are not perpendicular.

_____

_____

 Draw a line to match each figure to a real-world model.

8. ray   tip of a pin

9. plane   tabletop

10. intersecting lines   train tracks

11. line segment   spoke on a wheel

12. point   light from a flashlight

13. parallel lines   two roads that cross each other

Geometry

Review It! **When you plot points on a grid, remember these words:**

coordinate plane a grid made of two number lines called the x-axis and the y-axis

x-axis the horizontal (left to right) number line on a coordinate grid

y-axis the vertical (up and down) number line on a coordinate grid

ordered pair: a point where the x-axis and y-axis meet on a grid

(2, 3) is an ordered pair

x-coordinate ·········· ⌐········ y-coordinate

Geometry

Plot the point $(7, 4\frac{1}{2})$. Label it A.

Step 1   Start at the origin, $(0, 0)$.

Step 2   Move 7 units to the right using the x–coordinate.

Step 3   From there, move up $4\frac{1}{2}$ units using the y–coordinate.

Step 4   Make a dot on the point. Label it A.

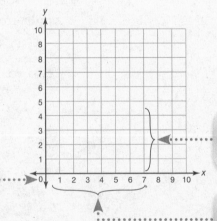

REMEMBER Always start at (0, 0).

THINK The y-coordinate is $4\frac{1}{2}$. Move $4\frac{1}{2}$ units up.

THINK The x-coordinate is 7. Move 7 units right.

So, point A is at (____, ____).

Try It!   Write the letter name of each point.

1. (5, 9) _____   **2.** (3, 8) _____

3. (3, 4) _____   **4.** (7, 5) _____

5. (2, 0) _____   **6.** (8, 3) _____

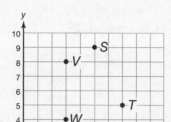

1.

Which way do you move 9 units?
up or to the right

Write the ordered pair for each point.

7. A _____   **8.** B _____

9. C _____   **10.** D _____

11. E _____   **12.** F _____

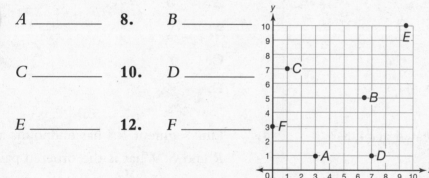

7.

How many units to the right from (0, 0) is *A*?
1, 3, or 4

Geometry

Use the ordered pair to plot each point.
Label each point with its letter.

13. J (1, 4)   **14.** K (9, 3½)

15. L (5, 2½)   **16.** M (4, 9)

17. N (0, 6)   **18.** P (8, 10)

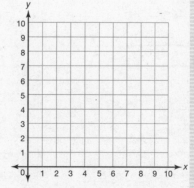

13.

In which direction do you move first?
to the right or up

Circle the answer for each question.

1. What ordered pair names point *X*?

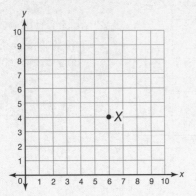

- **A.** (4, 6)
- **B.** (5, 4)
- **C.** (6, 4)
- **D.** (6, 3)

2. Which point is located at (4, 8)?

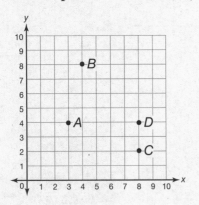

- **A.** point *A*
- **B.** point *B*
- **C.** point *C*
- **D.** point *D*

3. Which point is located at (0, 5)?

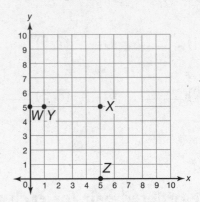

- **A.** *W*
- **B.** *X*
- **C.** *Y*
- **D.** *Z*

4. Line segment *RS* has endpoints at *R* and *S*. What is the ordered pair of point *S*?

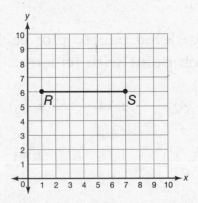

- **A.** (7, 6)
- **B.** (8, 6)
- **C.** (6, 7)
- **D.** (6, 5)

Geometry

Use the grid for Questions 5 and 6.

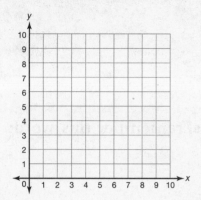

5. Plot a point at $(3\frac{1}{2}, 6)$ on the coordinate grid. Label it X.

6. *ABCD* is a rectangle. Point A is at $(2, 4)$, point B is at $(5, 4)$, and point C is at $(5, 1)$. What are the coordinates of point D? Use the grid to help you.

_____

Math Words   **Draw a line to match each word to its meaning.**

7. x-axis   the vertical number line on a grid

8.   ordered pair   a point where the x-axis and y-axis meet

9.   origin   the horizontal number line on a grid

10. y-axis $(0, 0)$ on a coordinate grid

Geometry

Patterns in Tables and Graphs

Review It! When you complete patterns, remember this word:

pattern a predictable arrangement of numbers or figures

The graph shows attendance of monthly Math Club meetings.

If the pattern continues, how many people will attend the meeting during Month 6?

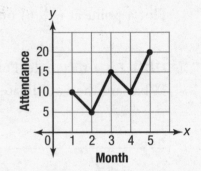

Step 1 Read the graph.

Complete the table of values.

x (month)	1	2	3	4	5
y (attendance)	10	5	15	10	20

> **REMEMBER** Look for the number on the vertical axis.

Step 2 Find the pattern.

For increasing attendance, add 10.

For decreasing attendance, subtract 5.

Step 3 Use the pattern to solve the problem.

$$20 \quad -5 \quad = \underline{\qquad}$$

month 5   rule   month 6

> **THINK** The rule is decrease 5, increase 10.

So, if the pattern continues, _____ people will attend the meeting during Month 6.

Try It!

Look for a pattern. Extend the pattern to find the missing number.

1.

Years	1	2	3	4	5	6
Sales	55	44	33	22	11	?

_____

1.

Which two operations should you consider?
addition
subtraction
multiplication
division

2.

Months	1	2	3	4	5	6
Books Read	1	3	6	10	15	?

_____

3.

Days	1	2	3	4	5	6
Minutes of Exercise	10	6	12	8	16	?

_____

4.

Hours	1	2	3	4	5	6
Temperatures	36	18	16	8	6	?

_____

The graph shows the estimated population growth of York, Pennsylvania. Use the graph for Questions 5 and 6.

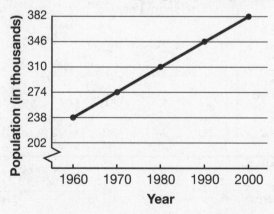

5. By how much does the population change every 10 years?
_____ thousand

5.

Which axis shows the pattern?
x-axis or *y*-axis

6. Predict the population of York for the year 2010.
_____ thousand

Algebra

1. A grocery store began asking its customers to donate canned foods for a charity food bank. This chart shows the number of cans donated from January through April.

Canned Food Donations

Month	Jan	Feb	Mar	Apr	May
Number of cans	8	24	72	216	?

If the pattern in the chart continues, how many cans should the store expect to receive in May?

A. 217   **C.** 288

B. 232   **D.** 432

2. Bernard records how many pushups he does each day in this chart.

Pushups

Day	1	2	3	4	5	6
Number of pushups	18	14	20	16	22	?

If the pattern in the chart continues, how many pushups will Bernard most likely do on Day 6?

A. 14   **C.** 18

B. 16   **D.** 26

3. Samantha is taking clarinet lessons. She records how many minutes she practices each day. This line graph shows the number of minutes she practiced each day during a six-day period.

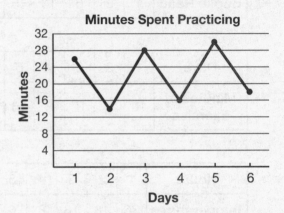

If the pattern shown in this graph continues, for how many minutes would Samantha most likely practice on Day 7?

A. 12

B. 14

C. 30

D. 32

4. A ball is dropped from 128 feet. This table shows how high it bounces following each contact with the ground.

Height of Bouncing Ball

Bounce	1	2	3	4	5	6
Height (in feet)	64	32	16	8	?	?

Part A How high will it go after the fifth and sixth bounces?

_____ ft and _____ ft

Part B Explain the steps you used to answer Part A.

_____

_____

_____

_____

Draw a line to match each word to its meaning.

5. pattern   a chart that shows a pattern that can be extended

6. table   a graph that can be used to make predictions

7. line graph   a predictable arrangement of numbers

Algebra

22 Rules for Patterns

Review It! Remember that a rule must work for all of the numbers in a pattern.

Find a rule for this input/output table.

Input Number	Output Number
12	6
24	18
36	30
48	42

Step 1   Look at each row of numbers.

           The output number is always less than the input number.

           So, test both subtraction and division. ◄••••••••••••••••••

> **REMEMBER** Addition and multiplication increase value. Subtraction and division decrease value.

Step 2   Use Row 1 to describe two possible rules.

           Subtract 6 from the input number.

           Divide the input number by 2.

Step 3   Test both rules against Row 2.

           $24 - 6 = 18$ $24 \div 2 = 12$

           The rule subtract 6 works.

Step 4   Check that the rule works in all other rows.

           $36 - 6 = $ _____

           $48 - 6 = $ _____

So, the rule for the table is _____ _____.

Try It!   Write the rule for the input/output table.

1.

Input Number	Output Number
2	30
4	32
6	34
8	36

2.

Input Number	Output Number
3	21
6	42
9	27
12	36

_____

_____

Ask Yourself

1.

Which works for Row 2?
Add 28.
Multiply by 15.

Algebra

Write the rule for the pattern.

3.   243, 27, 81, 9, . . .

4.   54, 51, 55, 52, 56, 53, . . .

_____

_____

3.

Which operations should you check?
+ and ×
or − and ÷

Start with 60. Use the rule to write the next four numbers.

5.   Divide by 4 to get the next number. Then add 5 to get the number after that. Repeat these steps.

6.   Multiply by 3 to get the next number. Then subtract 100 to get the number after that. Repeat these steps.

5.

Which gives the number after 60?
60 ÷ 4 or 60 + 5

_____

_____

Circle the answer for each question.

1. This table shows the number of volunteers helping in a soup kitchen each week.

Soup Kitchen Volunteers

Week	Number of Volunteers
1	3
2	4
3	2
4	3
5	1

Which describes a rule for the pattern in the table?

A. Add 1 to get the next number; then subtract 2 to get the number after that; repeat these steps.

B. Subtract 1 to get the next number; then add 2 to get the number after that; repeat these steps.

C. Add 1 to get the next number; then divide by 2 to get the number after that; repeat these steps.

D. Add 1 to get the next number; then add 2 to get the number after that; repeat these steps.

2. Which rule relates each input number to its output number?

Input Number	Output Number
6	3
12	6
18	9
24	12

A. Add 6 to each input number to get its output number.

B. Subtract 3 from each input number to get its output number.

C. Multiply each input number by 2 to get its output number.

D. Divide each input number by 2 to get its output number.

3. Which of the following describes a method that could be used to find the missing input number in the table below?

Input Number	Output Number
8	1
11	4
19	12
?	20

A. Add 9 to 19.

B. Add 8 to 19.

C. Add 7 to 20.

D. Subtract 4 from 20.

4. A pattern follows this rule:

Multiply the previous number by 4 to find the next number in the pattern; then subtract 12; repeat these steps.

Part A If the pattern starts with the number 5, what will the next six numbers in the pattern be? Fill in the chart below with those numbers.

Position in Pattern	1st number	2nd number	3rd number	4th number	5th number	6th number	7th number
Number	5						

Part B Explain or show how you used the rule to find the numbers in the pattern.

_____

_____

_____

_____

Draw a line to match each word to its meaning.

5. rule   the starting number for a rule

6. input number   the ending number for a rule

7. output number   words and numbers that describe how to get the next number in a pattern

Algebra

Matching Expressions and Equations to Situations

Review It! When you translate words into expressions, remember these phrases:

Operation	Word Phrases	Math Example
Addition	n plus 7 Add 7 to a n. 7 more than n the sum of 7 and n	$n + 7$
Subtraction	k take away 4 Subtract 4 from a k. 4 fewer than k 4 less than k	$k - 4$
Multiplication	2 times a number b twice a number b the product of 2 and b	$2b$
Division	a number x split evenly 10 ways Divide a number x by 10. x divided by 10 one tenth of a number	$x \div 10$

Write an expression that represents these words.

h less than 20

Step 1 Find the key words that describe the operation.
The key words are *less than*.

Step 2 Name the operation that *less than* describes. _____

Step 3 Write the expression that represents the words. _____

So, h less than 20 can be represented by the expression _____.

REMEMBER In both subtraction and division, the order of the numbers and variables is important.

Write the expression that represents the phrase.

1. the sum of 11 and y

_____

2. the product of p and 7

_____

3. the quotient of 5 and c

_____

4. 9 minus r

_____

5. 6 less than w

_____

6. v subtracted from 12

_____

7. Add 15 and h.

_____

8. half of x

_____

9. twice k

_____

10. g plus 9

_____

11. z times 4

_____

12. 19 divided by u

_____

13. 3 less than n

_____

14. 12 more than a

_____

15. 18 divided by b

_____

16. Multiply 11 and f.

_____

Algebra

Ask Yourself

1.

Which operation does "sum" represent?
addition
subtraction
multiplication
division

2.

For which two operations does order matter?
addition and muliplication
subtraction and division

On Your Own!   Circle the answer for each question.

1. Tom has 30 more baseball cards
    than Kathy. If k stands for the
    number of cards Kathy has, which
    expression stands for the number
    of cards Tom has?

    A. $k + 30$

    B. $30 - k$

    C. $k - 30$

    D. $\frac{30}{k}$

2. Mr. Fan has 5 acres to give to
    relatives. If r stands for the number
    of relatives Mr. Fan has, which
    expression stands for the number of
    acres each relative gets?

    A. $\frac{r}{5}$

    B. $5 \div r$

    C. $5 - r$

    D. $5r$

3. Which expression represents this
    phrase?

    half of c

    A. $2c$

    B. $c - \frac{1}{2}$

    C. $c + \frac{1}{2}$

    D. $\frac{c}{2}$

4. Rachel gets twice as many weeks
    vacation time as Mark. If w stands
    for the number of vacation weeks
    Mark gets, which stands for Rachel's
    vacation time?

    A. $2w$

    B. $\frac{w}{2}$

    C. $\frac{2}{w}$

    D. $2 + w$

5. Bob has 5 fewer fish than Leslie. If
    Leslie has x fish, how many does
    Bob have?

    A. $5 - x$

    B. $x - 5$

    C. $5 \div x$

    D. $x \div 5$

6. Kristin earns $15 for each necktie
    she makes. Which shows how much
    she earns for n neckties?

    A. $15 \div n$

    B. $\frac{n}{15}$

    C. $15n$

    D. $15 + n$

7. On a test, Angie was not sure if she should write "6 − *d*" or "*d* − 6" to represent the phrase "6 less than *d*."

  Part A   Which expression is correct?

  _____

  Part B   Explain how you determined your answer for Part A.

  _____

  _____

  _____

 Draw a line to match each phrase to its math meaning.

8.   8 more than *m*   8*m*

9. $\frac{8}{m}$ *m* − 8

10. *m* divided by 8   8 − *m*

11. 8 minus *m*   *m* + 8

12. the product of *m* and 8   8 ÷ *m*

13. 8 less than *m*   *m* ÷ 8

24 Solving Equations

Review It!

When you solve equations, remember these words:

equation a number sentence with an equal (=) sign

$$7 + 4 = 11, h - 9 = 22$$

variable a letter in an algebraic expression that stands for a number

operation	opposite operation
Addition	Subtraction
Subtraction	Addition
Multiplication	Division
Division	Multiplication

Solve the equation $v - 10 = 9$ for v.

Step 1 Add 10 to both sides:

$$v - 10 + 10 = 9 + 10 \longleftarrow$$

> **REMEMBER** Adding 10 is the opposite of subtracting 10.

Step 2 Simplify both sides.

$$v + 0 = 19$$

$$v = 19$$

Step 3 Substitute $v = 19$ into the equation to check.

$$v - 10 = 9$$

$$19 - 10 = 9$$

$$\underline{\hspace{2cm}} = 9 \longleftarrow$$

> **REMEMBER** If both sides of the equation are equal, the answer checks.

So, the solution to the equation $v - 10 = 9$ is $v = \underline{\hspace{1.5cm}}$.

 Solve each equation.

Ask Yourself

1. $\frac{a}{5} = 10$

2. $h + 3 = 21$

_____

_____

3. $8w = 44$

4. $y - 13 = 20$

_____

_____

5. $\frac{c}{6} = 12$

6. $10v = 90$

_____

_____

7. $n - 15 = 15$

8. $k + 20 = 40$

_____

_____

9. $5b = 105$

10. $27 + r = 62$

_____

_____

11. $\frac{s}{7} = 4$

12. $g - 8 = 32$

_____

_____

13. $39 + d = 100$

14. $x - 64 = 100$

_____

_____

15. $\frac{n}{15} = 5$

16. $25y = 300$

_____

_____

1.

Which will isolate
the variable?
Multiply both sides of
the equation by 5.
Multiply both sides of
the equation by 10.

2.

Which operation will
isolate the variable?
addition
subtraction
multiplication
division

Algebra

On Your Own!

Circle the answer for each question.

1. How could you isolate the variable, r, in this equation?

   $r - 18 = 20$

   A. Add 18 to both sides of the equation.

   B. Subtract 18 from both sides of the equation.

   C. Add 20 to both sides of the equation.

   D. Subtract 20 from both sides of the equation.

2. How could you isolate the variable, m, in this equation?

   $\frac{m}{4} = 12$

   A. Multiply both sides of the equation by 4.

   B. Divide both sides of the equation by 4.

   C. Multiply both sides of the equation by 12.

   D. Divide both sides of the equation by 12.

3. Solve for y: $10 + y = 40$

   A. 4

   B. 30

   C. 50

   D. 100

4. Solve for g: $20g = 6$

   A. 0.3   C. 26

   B. 14   D. 120

5. Solve for j: $7j = 21$

   A. $\frac{1}{3}$

   B. 3

   C. 14

   D. 28

6. Solve for c: $\frac{c}{9} = 6$

   A. $\frac{2}{3}$

   B. 1.5

   C. 3

   D. 54

7. Solve for q: $q - 30 = 75$

   A. 2.5

   B. 45

   C. 105

   D. 2,250

8. Solve for k: $k + 25 = 40$

   A. 1.6

   B. 15

   C. 65

   D. 1,000

9. Leon solved an equation for *t*. His solution is shown below.

$$t - 40 = 55$$

$$t - 40 + 40 = 55 - 40$$

$$t = 15$$

Part A His solution contains an error. Solve the equation $t - 40 = 55$ and determine the correct answer.

_____

Part B Explain what error Leon made and what he could have done differently to solve the problem.

_____

_____

_____

 Draw a line to match each word to its meaning.

10. isolate   an operation that undoes another operation

11. opposite operation   a letter in an algebraic expression that stands for a number

12. equation   separate something from all other things

13. variable   a number sentence with an equal sign

Bar, Line, and Circle Graphs

Review It! When you read and interpret graphs, remember these words:

bar graph a graph that uses bars (rectangles) of different lengths to compare data

circle graph divides a circle into regions, each representing a part of a whole

line graph a graph that uses line segments to show trends or changes in data over time

---

The graph shows the number of games won each year for 4 years. Find the difference between the least and most number of games won.

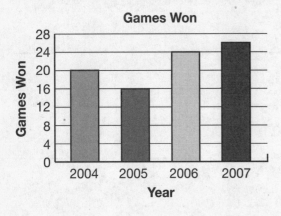

THINK A short bar shows fewer games than a long bar.

Step 1 Which year shows the least number of games won? _____

How many games did the team win that year? _____

Step 2 Which year shows the greatest number of games won? _____

How many games did the team win that year? _____

Step 3 Subtract to find the difference. _____ − _____ = _____

So, the difference between the least and most number of games won is _____.

The bar graph at the right shows how students in Ms. Douglass's class get to school. Use the bar graph to answer Questions 1–3.

1. Which type of transportation was most popular?

_____

2. How many students ride a bike?

_____

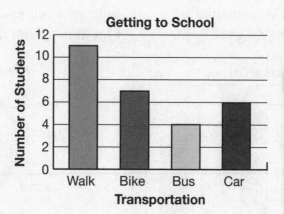

Getting to School

3. How many students are in Ms. Douglass's class?

_____

The circle graph at the right shows how Kim plans to spend her earnings. Use the circle graph to answer Questions 4–6.

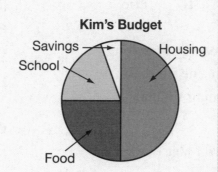

Kim's Budget

4. What will Kim spend the most money on?

_____

5. What fraction of her money will she spend on food?

_____

6. Which item or items will she spend less money on than food?

_____

Circle the answer for each question.

1. The bar graph shows the heights of 4 young children. Which child is 6 inches taller than Amy?

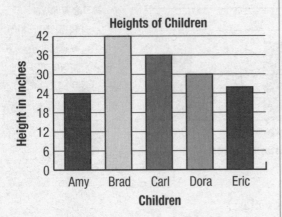

Heights of Children

A. Brad   C. Dora

B. Carl   D. Eric

2. Each year Nora records how long it takes her to run one mile. What might be her running time at 14 years old?

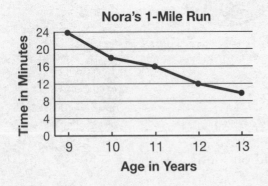

Nora's 1-Mile Run

A. 8 minutes

B. 10 minutes

C. 12 minutes

D. 14 minutes

The circle graph shows how Kirk spends his time after school. Use the circle graph for Questions 3 and 4.

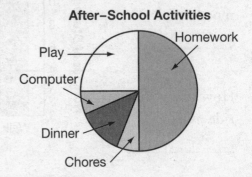

After–School Activities

3. On which activity does Kirk spend half his time?

A. Chores

B. Dinner

C. Homework

D. Play

4. On what does Kirk spend half as much time as play?

A. Chores

B. Computer

C. Dinner

D. Homework

5. The graph shows the amount of money Jill earned babysitting. The data shows January through June.

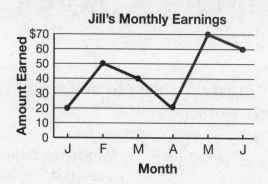

Part A How much did Jill earn in the first three months of the year?

_____

Part B Explain with words and/or numbers how you know your answer to Part A is correct.

_____

_____

_____

 Draw a line to match each word to its meaning.

6. data   a graph that divides a circle into regions that represent a part of a whole

7. bar graph   information with numbers

8. line graph   a graph that uses a crooked or bent line to show changes in data over time

9. circle graph   a graph that uses rectangles of different lengths to compare data

LESSON 26 Line Plots and Frequency Tables

Review It! When you use data in tables and charts, remember these words:

line plot data shown by Xs on a number line

frequency table a table that shows grouped data with tally marks and numbers that represent them

---

This line plot shows ages of children registered at summer camp. Organize the data in a frequency table.

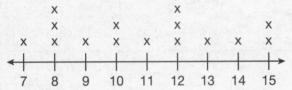

Ages of Children at Camp

REMEMBER The fifth tally mark goes across the first four tally marks.

Step 1 Make one tally mark for each X in the line plot.

Step 2 Then, count the number of tallies in each row. Write the number of tallies in the frequency column.

Ages of Children at Camp

Ages	Tally	Frequency
7–9	⊪⊪	5
10–12	⊪⊪ I	6
13–15	IIII	4

So, there are _____ children ages 7–9, _____ children ages 10–12, and _____ children ages 13–15.

Make a frequency table from the data.

1. 12, 12, 13, 13, 10, 9, 12, 13, 8

2. 52, 54, 51, 55, 56, 48, 52, 57, 59, 58, 50, 50, 51, 55

Ages of Moviegoers		
Age	Tally	Frequency
8–9		
10–11		
12–13		

Height in Inches		
Height	Tally	Frequency
48–51		
52–55		
56–59		

3. 86, 90, 100, 98, 105, 99, 102, 88, 109, 105, 101, 98, 95, 90, 91, 89

4. 90, 100, 91, 97, 65, 85, 72, 88, 81, 90, 85, 84, 82, 98, 89, 94, 89, 75, 77, 81, 76, 83

Weight in Pounds		
Weight	Tally	Frequency
86–91		
92–97		
98–103		
104–109		

Test Scores		
Height	Tally	Frequency
61–70		
71–80		
81–90		
91–100		

1. What is the tally for ages 12–13? IIII or ⊞

Use the data in Question 1.

5. Make a line plot.

Ages of Moviegoers

8   9   10   11   12   13

5. What is the least number on the number line? 0 or 8

Circle the answer for each question.

1. This data show high temperatures in degrees Fahrenheit for one week in December.

43, 45, 41, 44, 47, 45, 39

Which frequency table represents all of this data?

A.

Temperatures in °F	
Temperature	Frequency
39–41	2
42–44	3
45–47	2

B.

Temperatures in °F	
Temperature	Frequency
39–41	2
42–44	2
45–47	3

C.

Temperatures in °F	
Temperature	Frequency
39–41	2
42–44	3
45–47	1

D.

Temperatures in °F	
Temperature	Frequency
39–41	2
42–44	1
45–47	3

Audra wants to display this data in a line plot. Use this data for Questions 2–4.

Ages of Pre-School Children	
Age in Years	Number of Children
1	3
2	4
3	7
4	2

2. What is the frequency for the shortest bar?

A. 1

B. 2

C. 3

D. 4

3. Which age would have the longest bar?

A. 1

B. 2

C. 3

D. 7

4. How many Xs will show on the line plot altogether?

A. 4   C. 10

B. 7   D. 16

5. Draw tally marks to represent a frequency of 14. _____

6. This table shows the ages of cats that Dr. Pettery cares for.

Ages of Cats	
Years	Frequency
0–4	7
5–9	10
10–14	8
15–19	4

Pandora is a cat that Dr. Pettery cares for. She is 8 years old. How many other cats are in her category? _____

 Fill in the blanks.

7. A _____ _____ shows grouped data with tally marks or numbers that represent them.

8. A _____ _____ shows frequency with Xs on a number line.

LESSON 27 Double Bar Graphs

 **Review It!** When you graph data, remember this word:

double bar graph a bar graph that has two bars for each category

The graph below shows the length and width of Indiana, Ohio, and Pennsylvania.

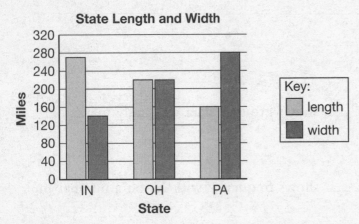

Which state has the greatest difference between width and length?

Step 1 Read the key.

The light gray bar stands for _____. The dark gray bar stands for _____.

Step 2 Subtract the length and width for each state. ◄············· **REMEMBER** Look how far up the vertical axis each bar goes.

Indiana: $270 - 140 = 130$

Ohio: $220 - 220 = 0$

Pennsylvania: _____ − _____ = _____

Step 3 Compare differences.

So, the state with the greatest difference between length and width is _____.

Use this double bar graph to answer Questions 1–5.

Pennsylvania Average High and Low Temperatures

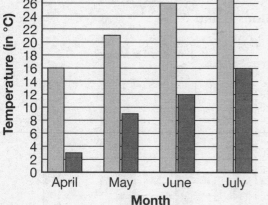

Key:
☐ high temperature
■ low temperature

1. What is the greatest difference between average high and low temperatures within a month?

_____

2. What is the change in average high temperatures between April and May?

_____

3. Which month has the least difference between its average high and low temperatures?

_____

4. How much does the average high temperature change from April to July?

_____

5. How much does the average low temperature change from April to July?

_____

1.

Which should you use to check April?

16 − 3 or 30 − 16

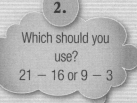

2.

Which should you use?

21 − 16 or 9 − 3

Circle the answer for each question.

1. This table shows the number of boys and the number of girls who enrolled in different sports camps.

Summer Sports Camp Enrollment		
	Boys	Girls
Tennis	50	50
Basketball	10	20
Baseball/Softball	20	30

Which graph shows the same data?

A.
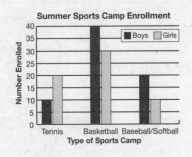

B.
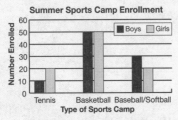

C.

D.

Jasper is a server at a popular restaurant. He recorded his tip earnings in the graph below. Use the double bar graph to answer Questions 2 and 3.

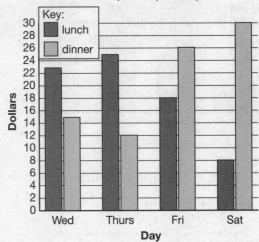

2. When did Jasper make $23 in tips?

   A. Wednesday lunch

   B. Wednesday dinner

   C. Thursday dinner

   D. Saturday lunch

3. On which day did Jasper make the greatest amount in tips?

   A. Wednesday

   B. Thursday

   C. Friday

   D. Saturday

4. Philip mows lawns and trims bushes. He recorded his earnings in the table. Then he made the double bar graph.

Philip's Yard Service Income			
	Week 1	**Week 2**	**Week 3**
Mowing	40	100	80
Trimming	120	60	80

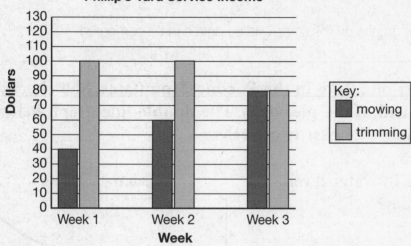

Philip's graph is incorrect. Explain what you would do to change the graph to match the table.

_____

_____

_____

Math Words

Draw a line to match each word to its meaning.

5. double bar graph   information with numbers

6. key   a guide that shows what each bar stands for

7. data   a bar graph that has two or more bars for each category

LESSON 28 Double Line Graphs

Review It!

When you use graphs, remember this word:

double line graph two line graphs on the same grid so data can be compared

Shannon owns a resort on a lake in the Pocono Mountains. She checks the water level at the end of the pier daily. The double line graph below compares water levels for the past two weeks.

What is the difference in water levels from Tuesday to Tuesday?

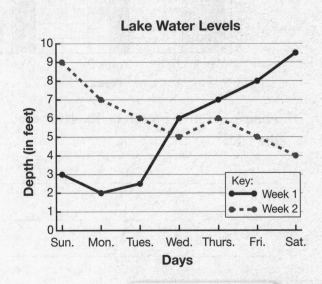

Lake Water Levels

Step 1 Read the key.

The solid line stands for

_____.

The dashed line stands for

_____.

Step 2 Find the two water levels for Tuesday. ◄···············

Week 1 water level: $2\frac{1}{2}$ feet

Week 2 water level: 6 feet

REMEMBER Look how far up the vertical axis each line goes.

Step 3 Find the difference.

$6 - 2\frac{1}{2} =$ _____

So, the difference in water levels from Tuesday to Tuesday is _____ feet.

Try It!

Charles made this graph to display temperatures from April through October in the Pocono Mountains. Use the graph to answer Questions 1–5.

 **Ask Yourself**

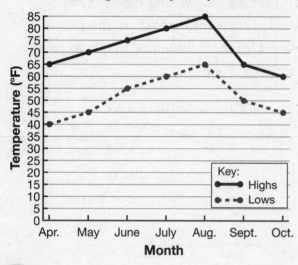

Average Monthly Temperatures

Key:
━━ Highs
┅┅ Lows

1. What is the greatest difference between average high and low temperatures within a month?

_____

2. What is the change in average high temperatures between August and October?

_____

3. Between which two months is the greatest drop in high temperatures? _____ and _____

4. How much does the average high temperature change from April to August?

_____

5. How much does the average low temperature change from April to August?

_____

1.

Which should you use to check April?
65 — 40 or 70 — 65

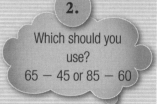

2.

Which should you use?
65 — 45 or 85 — 60

Data Analysis and Probability

Circle the answer for each question.

1.   This table shows the average weights for girls and boys.

Average Weights for Ages 10–16		
Age	Girls' Weights	Boys' Weights
10	70	70
12	95	88
14	109	112
16	118	135

Which graph shows the same data?

A.
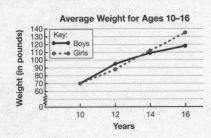

B.
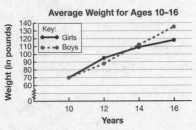

C.
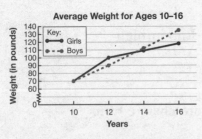

D.
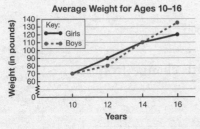

Keith and Robin are servers at a popular restaurant. Jane serves the lunch crowd. Keith serves the evening crowd. They recorded their tip earnings in the graph below. Use the double line graph to answer Questions 2 and 3.

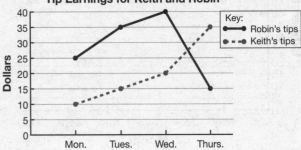

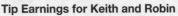

2.   What was the least that Robin made in tips for one day?

A. $10

B. $15

C. $25

D. $40

3.   On which day did Keith and Robin earn the most in combined tips?

A.   Monday

B.   Tuesday

C.   Wednesday

D.   Thursday

4. Nancy planted a sunflower on each side of her yard. She measured and recorded their height in inches in this table. Then she graphed her data in the double line graph.

Nancy's Sunflowers			
	Week 2	**Week 4**	**Week 6**
East flower	9	18	27
West flower	3	12	24

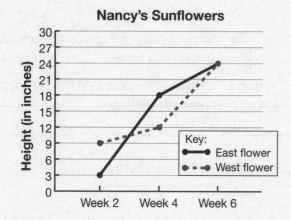

Nancy's graph is not correct. Explain what you would do to change the graph to match the table.

_____

_____

_____

Math Words

Draw a line to match each word to its meaning.

5. double line graph   a graph on a grid with a line to stand for the change in each set of data

6. key   a guide that shows what each line on a double line graph stands for

7. line graph   two or more line graphs on the same grid so data can be compared

Mean, Median, Mode, and Range

Review It!

When you compute statistics, remember these words:

mean the sum of the data values divided by the number of data values

median the middle number in an ordered set of data

mode the data item that appears more often than any other data item

range the difference between the greatest and least numbers in a data set

---

Find the mean, median, mode, and range of the set of data.
9, 3, 14, 3, 10, 3

Step 1 To find the **mean**, first find the sum of the data.

$9 + 3 + 14 + 3 + 10 + 3 =$ _____

How many numbers are in the data set? _____

Divide the sum by the number in the data set. _____ ÷ _____ = _____

So, the mean is _____.

Step 2 To find the **median**, first order the data from least to greatest: 3, 3, 3, 9, 10, 14.

What is the median? _____ ◄·····················

> **THINK** There is no single middle number. There are two middle numbers, so add them and divide by 2.

Step 3 To find the **mode**, look for the data item that appears more often than the others.

The mode is _____. ◄·····················

> **REMEMBER** Not every set of data has a mode.

Step 4 Find the **range** by subtracting.

greatest number   least number
↓   ↓
14   –   3   = _____

So, the mean is _____, the median is _____, the mode is _____, and the range is _____.

Find the mean, median, mode, and range for each data set.

 Ask Yourself

1. 5, 4, 8, 10, 9, 2, 4

mean = _____

median = _____

mode = _____

range = _____

2. 16, 16, 16, 16

mean = _____

median = _____

mode = _____

range = _____

1.

How many numbers are in the data set?
7 or 8

3. 5, 5, 8, 11, 1, 0, 10, 9, 5, 2

mean = _____

median = _____

mode = _____

range = _____

4. 22, 9, 40, 38, 35, 36

mean = _____

median = _____

mode = _____

range = _____

5.

Which will give the highest price?
$24 + $6.75
$24 − $6.75

Solve.

5. The range of prices of CDs at Wolfy's Discount Discs is $24. The lowest price is $6.75. What is the highest price?

_____

6. Two-thirds of Sandra's class earned 85 on the last spelling quiz. Half of the rest of the class earned scores below 85. The remaining students earned scores above 85. What was the median score?

_____

6.

What is the median score?
middle number
difference of two numbers

Data Analysis and Probability

On Your Own!

Circle the answer for each question.

Use this data to answer Questions 1–4.

Sarah's math test scores this year are 95, 74, 83, 95, 89, 83, 98, 100, 95, and 90.

1. What is her range of scores?

   A. 5   **C.** 22

   B. 16   **D.** 26

2. What is the median score?

   A. 50

   B. 86

   C. 90.2

   D. 92.5

3. What is the mode?

   A. 83   **C.** 98

   B. 95   **D.** 100

4. What is the mean?

   A. 26

   B. 90.2

   C. 92.5

   D. 95

Use this data to answer Questions 5–8.

Last week's daily high temperatures were 56°, 63°, 62°, 60°, 55°, 56°, and 61°.

5. What is the mean high temperature?

   A. 58°   **C.** 61°

   B. 59°   **D.** 63°

6. What is the mode?

   A. no mode

   B. 55°

   C. 56°

   D. 60°

7. What is the median?

   A. 58°   **C.** 61°

   B. 59°   **D.** 63°

8. What is the range?

   A. 2

   B. 5

   C. 6

   D. 8

9. Grant recorded his math quiz scores for the first marking period.
60, 88, 90, 100, 88, 94

His teacher says he can use the mean, median, mode, or range of these scores for his final grade.

Part A Which should he choose?

_____

Part B Explain your choice. Use words and/or numbers to support your explanation.

_____

_____

_____

_____

Draw a line to match each word to its meaning.

10. mean   the difference between the greatest and least in a data set

11. median   the data item that occurs more than any other data item

12. mode   the middle number in an ordered data set

13. range   the sum of the data values divided by the number of data values

LESSON 30 Probability

Review It! When you compute probabilities, remember these words:

probability a number between 0 and 1 that shows how likely a certain outcome is

outcome something that could happen in an event

One outcome of rolling a number cube is 5.

sample space a list of all possible outcomes of an event

The sample space of rolling a number cube is **1, 2, 3, 4, 5, or 6.**

Ron put 6 red marbles, 4 green marbles, and 10 blue marbles in a bag. Find the probability of selecting a red marble.

Step 1 Find the number of possible outcomes.

$6 + 4 + 10 =$ _____ ◄ ·············

THINK Each marble is a possible outcome.

Step 2 How many of the outcomes are favorable outcomes? _____

Step 3 Write the probability ratio.

THINK Red is favorable. How many are red?

$$\text{probability} = \frac{\text{favorable outcomes}}{\text{total possible outcomes}} = \underline{\hspace{1cm}}$$

Step 4 Simplify the ratio. _____

So, the probability of selecting a red marble at random is _____.

Try It! Each letter for the word RHINOCEROS is put on a separate card and placed in a bag. Then one card is selected at random. Find the probability of choosing the letter.

 **Ask Yourself**

1. S

2. O

3. R
_____   _____   _____

4. a vowel (A, E, I, O, or U)

5. a consonant (not a vowel)

6. P
_____
_____   _____

1.

What is the total number of outcomes?
8 or 10

A number cube labeled 1–6 is tossed. Find the probability of the outcome.

7. 4

8. 1

9. an even number
_____   _____   _____

10. a number divisible by 3

11. an odd number

12. 10
_____   _____   _____

7.

How many times is 4 on the number cube?
1 or 4

Solve.

13. Lois takes 5 cards and numbers them from 10 to 14. She will shuffle them and pick one without looking. What are all possible outcomes of this event?

14. A bag holds 3 red marbles, 9 blue marbles and 4 yellow marbles. A marble will be picked without looking. What is the sample space for this event?

17.

How many different outcomes are possible?
5 or 14

_____   _____

Data Analysis and Probability

Circle the answer for each question.

Use the following for Questions 1–4.

A bag holds 5 yellow cubes, 6 orange cubes, 1 blue cube and 8 red cubes.

1. What is the sample space?

   A. the bag

   B. {5, 6, 2, 7}

   C. {yellow, orange, red}

   D. {yellow, orange, blue, red}

2. Which is a possible outcome of picking one cube at random?

   A. blue

   B. green

   C. purple

   D. pink

3. What is the probability of picking an orange cube at random?

   A. $\frac{1}{20}$ C. $\frac{3}{10}$

   B. $\frac{1}{6}$ D. $\frac{3}{7}$

4. Which color is the most likely to be picked at random?

   A. blue   C. red

   B. orange   D. yellow

5. There are 9 girls and 7 boys as guests at Marla's birthday party. She will place all their names in a bag. Then she will draw one at random to win a prize. What is the probability it will show a boy's name?

   A. $\frac{7}{16}$ C. $\frac{7}{9}$

   B. $\frac{9}{16}$ D. $\frac{9}{7}$

6. Dan has cards numbered from 1 to 20. He will shuffle them and pick a card at random. What is the probability that he will choose a card divisible by 3?

   A. $\frac{3}{20}$ C. $\frac{1}{3}$

   B. $\frac{3}{10}$ D. $\frac{1}{2}$

7. A number cube is numbered from 1 to 6. What is the probability of tossing a prime number?

   A. $\frac{1}{6}$

   B. $\frac{1}{3}$

   C. $\frac{1}{2}$

   D. $\frac{2}{3}$

8.   The spinner below is divided into six equal parts.

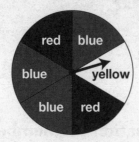

Part A   What is the probability of landing on blue?

_____

Part B   Use words and/or numbers to explain how you solved the problem.

_____

_____

_____

Math Words   **Draw a line to match each word to its meaning.**

9.   random   a list of all possible outcomes of an event

10.   probability   something that could happen in an event

11.   outcome   with no planned outcome

12.   sample space   how likely an outcome will occur

LESSON 31 Combinations

Review It! When you use combinations, remember these words:

arrangements different ways to order a group or set of items

tree diagram an array used to find the number of possible combinations

---

Arthur is making a sandwich. He can choose between whole wheat or rye bread, cheddar or Swiss cheese, and tomato or lettuce vegetable. How many different choices does he have?

Step 1 Make a tree diagram.

The categories for choices are *Bread, Cheese,* and *Vegetables.*

Step 2 Fill in the tree diagram. ◄···················· **THINK** The number of branches to each category matches the number of choices in that category.

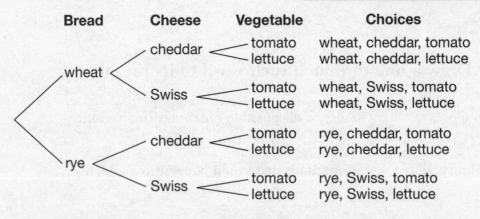

Bread	Cheese	Vegetable	Choices
wheat	cheddar	tomato	wheat, cheddar, tomato
		lettuce	wheat, cheddar, lettuce
	Swiss	tomato	wheat, Swiss, tomato
		lettuce	wheat, Swiss, lettuce
rye	cheddar	tomato	rye, cheddar, tomato
		lettuce	rye, cheddar, lettuce
	Swiss	tomato	rye, Swiss, tomato
		lettuce	rye, Swiss, lettuce

Step 3 Count the number of rows in the choices column to find the number of choices Arthur has.

So, Arthur has _____ different choices for his sandwich.

Data Analysis and Probability

Draw a tree diagram to solve.

1. List all the different ways that Amy, Brad, and Carli can stand in line.

1.

How many different people could be first?
1 or 3

_____

2. Priscilla has black, navy, and brown slacks. She has sweaters that are turquoise, white, and pink. How many different outfits does she have?

2.

How many different outfits are just with black slacks?
1 or 3

_____

3. Lockers for Ms. Grable's classroom are lettered A, B, or C followed by a number that is 1, 2, 3, 4, 5, or 6. How many different lockers are there?

_____

4. Mr. Emerson's classroom lockers are lettered D or E followed by a number that is 0, 1, 2, 3, 4, 5, 6, 7, 8, or 9. How many different lockers does Mr. Emerson's class have?

_____

Data Analysis and Probability

Circle the answer for each question.

1. A health food lunch cafe offers a choice of salad or sandwich. For dessert, it offers a choice of apple, orange, or pear. For drink, it offers a choice of milk, water or juice. How many different lunches does it offer?

   A. 1

   B. 3

   C. 8

   D. 18

2. For a salad, Bill has a choice of iceberg or romaine lettuce. He can choose one additional ingredient of grated cheese, radishes, carrots, or tomatoes. For dressing, he can choose either creamy Italian or ranch. How many different salads are possible?

   A. 3

   B. 8

   C. 12

   D. 16

3. Cora wants to buy a hat at one store, a scarf at another store, and a pair of gloves at a third store. In how many different ways could she order her purchases?

   A. 2   C. 6

   B. 3   D. 12

4. Mrs. Henry is hanging pictures of her three children in a line on a wall. In how many different arrangements could she hang the pictures?

   A. 1

   B. 3

   C. 6

   D. 12

5. Chester ordered soup and a sandwich for lunch at a restaurant. There are 2 different kinds of soup and 8 different kinds of sandwiches. How many different choices did he have?

   A. 16

   B. 10

   C. 8

   D. 2

6. T-shirts at Mike's Shop have short or long sleeves. They come in colors white, red, and green. They come in sizes small, medium, and large. How many different choices of t-shirts are at Mike's Shop?

   A. 18

   B. 16

   C. 8

   D. 4

7. Blaine is choosing a hat and mittens for his sister's birthday. The hats come in green, red, blue, and ivory. The mittens come in green, red, blue, ivory, and yellow.

Part A List the different combinations of hat and mittens. Use G for green, R for red, B for blue, I for ivory, and Y for yellow. List green hat and yellow mittens as GY.

_____

_____

_____

Part B How many different combinations are there? _____

Fill in the blanks.

8. One way to order items is a(n) _____.

9. You can use a(n) _____ _____ to find all the different combinations of things.

Data Analysis and Probability

Math Words

acute angle an angle that measures between 0° and 90° (Lesson 13)

acute triangle a three-sided polygon with three acute angles (Lesson 15)

arrangements different ways to order a group or set of items (Lesson 31)

Associative Property if three numbers are added or if three numbers are multiplied, the result is the same if the grouping of the number is changed (Lesson 4)

bar graph a graph that uses bars (rectangles) of different lengths to compare data (Lesson 25)

circle graph divides a circle into regions, each representing a part of a whole (Lesson 25)

Commutative Property if two numbers are added or multiplied, the result is the same if the positions are switched (Lesson 4)

compatible numbers numbers that are easy to compute mentally

coordinate plane a grid made of two number lines called the *x*-axis and the *y*-axis (Lesson 20)

D **decimal** a number with a decimal point (Lesson 6)

denominator the bottom part of a fraction (Lesson 6)

divisible a number is divisible by a second number if the second number evenly divides into the first number (Lesson 2)

double bar graph a bar graph that has two bars for each category (Lesson 27)

double line graph two line graphs on the same grid so data can be compared (Lesson 28)

E **elapsed time** the amount of time that passes from the start to the end of an event (Lesson 11)

equation a number sentence with an equal (=) sign (Lesson 24)

equilateral triangle a three-sided polygon with three equal sides (Lesson 15)

equivalent numbers in different forms that have the same value (Lesson 6)

estimate a number that is close to the exact answer (Lesson 10)

exponent a number that tells the number of equal factors (Lesson 3)

factor number that divides evenly into another number (Lesson 1)

fraction a number that compares a part to a whole or a part to a part (Lesson 5)

frequency table a table that shows grouped data with tally marks and numbers that represent them (Lesson 26)

 greatest common factor (GCF) the greatest number that divides evenly into two or more numbers (Lesson 1)

 hypotenuse the longest side of a right triangle, located across from the right angle (Lesson 15)

 Identity Property a number remains unchanged if 0 is added to it; a number remains unchanged if it is multiplied by 1 (Lesson 4)

improper fraction a fraction with a value greater than or equal to 1 (Lesson 5)

intersecting lines two or more lines that meet at a point (Lesson 19)

irregular polygon any polygon that is not regular (Lesson 14)

isosceles triangle a three-sided polygon with two equal sides (Lesson 15)

 least common multiple (LCM) the least number that is a multiple of two numbers (Lesson 1)

leg one of the two shorter sides of a right triangle (Lesson 15)

line graph a graph that uses line segments to show trends or changes in data over time (Lesson 25)

line one straight string of points that extends forever in both directions (Lesson 19)

line plot data shown by Xs on a number line (Lesson 26)

line segment part of a line between two endpoints (Lesson 19)

 mean the sum of data divided by the number of items in the data set (Lesson 29)

median the middle number in an ordered set of data (Lesson 29)

mixed number a number with a whole number part and a fraction part (Lesson 5)

mode the data item that appears more often than any other data item (Lesson 29)

multiple the product of a number and a counting number (Lesson 1)

 numerator the top part of a fraction (Lesson 6)

obtuse angle an angle that measures between 90° and 180° (Lesson 13)

obtuse triangle a three-sided polygon with one obtuse angle (Lesson 15)

ordered pair a point where the *x*-axis and *y*-axis meet on a grid (Lesson 20)

outcome something that could happen in an event (Lesson 30)

parallel (∥) lines two or more lines in one plane that never intersect (Lesson 19)

parallel sides sides that are always the same distance apart (Lesson 17)

parallelogram a quadrilateral with opposite sides parallel and equal in length (Lesson 17)

pattern a predictable arrangement of numbers or figures (Lesson 21)

percent a ratio of a number to 100 (Lesson 7)

perimeter distance around a polygon found by adding the lengths of its sides (Lesson 14)

perpendicular (⊥) lines two lines that intersect to form right angles (Lesson 19)

plane a set of points that form a flat surface (Lesson 19)

polygon a figure made with line segments that enclose a space (Lesson 14)

probability how likely an outcome will occur (Lesson 30)

quadrilateral any polygon with 4 sides (Lesson 17)

range the difference between the greatest and least numbers in a data set (Lesson 29)

reciprocal two numbers that have a product of 1 (Lesson 9)

rectangle a parallelogram with 4 right angles (Lesson 17)

regular polygon a polygon with equal sides and equal angles (Lesson 14)

repeating decimal numbers to the right of a decimal point that repeat continuously in a pattern (Lesson 6)

rhombus a parallelogram with 4 equal sides (Lesson 17)

right angle an angle that measures exactly 90° (Lesson 13)

right triangle a three-sided polygon with one right angle (Lesson 15)

sample space a list of all possible outcomes of an event (Lesson 30)

scalene triangle a three-sided polygon with all sides having different lengths (Lesson 15)

square a parallelogram with 4 right angles and 4 equal sides (Lesson 17)

 trapezoid a quadrilateral with just one pair of parallel sides (Lesson 17)

tree diagram an array used to find the number of possible combinations (Lesson 31)

 variable a letter in an algebraic expression that stands for a number (Lesson 24)

vertex the "corner" of an angle (Lesson 13)

 x-axis the horizontal (left to right) number line on a coordinate grid (Lesson 20)

 y-axis the vertical (up and down) number line on a coordinate grid (Lesson 20)

My Math Words

_____	_____	_____
_____	_____	_____
_____	_____	_____
_____	_____	_____
_____	_____	_____
_____	_____	_____
_____	_____	_____
_____	_____	_____
_____	_____	_____
_____	_____	_____
_____	_____	_____